The Poacher and the Gamekeeper

Leadership for Risk Mitigation in Occupational Health and Safety

Michael Welham and Stewart Risk

Published in 2004 by Total Control (Anglia) Ltd
Colney Hall
Watton Road
Norwich NR4 7TY

www.totalcontrolanglia.co.uk

The views and opinions expressed within this book do not reflect those of either the Health and Safety Executive or the judiciary. While every care has been taken in the writing and editing of this book, readers should be aware that only Acts of Parliament and Statutory Instruments have the force of the law, and only the courts can authoritatively interpret the law.

Whilst every care has been taken to ensure the accuracy of the contents of this work, no responsibility for loss occasioned to any person acting or refraining from action as a result of any statement in it cannot be accepted by the authors or publisher.

ISBN 0 953 1889 1 4

Printed and bound in Great Britain by Antony Rowe Ltd, Chippenham, Wiltshire

Preface

There are shelves full of health and safety instructions, guidance, research projects, academic papers and books – all valuable and informative – so who has the answers? The simple answer is nobody, and while the authors, Michael Welham and Stewart Risk, have long been involved with health and safety in the workplace and promote safe working practices they do not have the definitive answer. However, both have management responsibilities, albeit in opposing vistas of health and safety and have intertwined career paths, and it is their combined experiences, which makes this book unique.

The authors first met when they worked in the North Sea oil and gas industry in the 1970s which was in a boom time and commercial diving, while dangerous, was a vital part of the industry.

After a successful period as an active diver Michael encountered a life-threatening situation, which was a mixture of supervisory failure and fellow worker complacency. It was time to move on and he had the fortune to be headhunted to join BRITOIL Plc which led him to be involved in safety, planning and operations of the companies subsea operations in the North Sea. He prepared emergency procedures and carried out safety audits. Stewart remained with Subsea Offshore Ltd and became base manager in Great Yarmouth responsible for a turnover of £1m. He worked his way up to Managing Director with a staff of over 1,000 personnel and a turnover of £150m. During this time, he focused on safety, operational efficiency and quality, the company achieving ISO 9001 accreditation for quality and ISO 14001, the accreditation for environmental management. He was recognised by BP for his personal commitment and leadership in safety.

Michael moved to the Health and Safety Executive in 1989 to manage a team of operational health and safety Inspectors.

Stewart became Managing Director of DSND Subsea Ltd where his focus was to improve DSND's safety performance allowing the company to achieve a leadership position for safety performance. This was rewarded in 2001 when the company won a ROSPA Gold Award for safety on first application. In 2001 he was promoted to the position of Vice President and managed a project to standardise worldwide business processes. A notable achievement includes the successful safe raising of the Russian nuclear submarine, the *Kursk*. In 2002, DSND merged with Halliburton Subsea to form Subsea 7 and Stewart was made Vice President of health, safety, environment and quality with the responsibility for delivering the new company's standardised corporate processes throughout the global operations. In 2003 he was headhunted to take up a new position sponsored by the Department of Trade and Industry and Scottish Enterprise to become Chief Executive of *Resource* an organisation tasked with promoting opportunities and networking for business in the environmental sector.

It will be seen that both authors have come from an industrial background where death at work was commonplace and they have, therefore, experienced the consequences of management failures. They have also seen the positive aspects of leadership management with regard to health and safety and that is the basis of this book. It is planned that as of January 2005 the authors will combine their substantial expertise and work to promote workplace health and safety based upon the leadership management principles.

It is important to state that workplace health and safety is generic and involves every conceivable business and undertaking. What create the difference are the hazards an undertaking faces or creates through its activities. The key element is that once the hazards are known it is the identification of the risks and the systems to control or eliminate the risks that is the every day task. The fact that the authors focus on a high risk and specialist industry is not important, the principles apply to all undertakings.

With the pending changes in the law with regard to corporate killing, individual manslaughter and the identification of director responsible for health and safety, it is necessary for senior management to understand the implications these will have on them. The foundation of the corporate killing offence is expected to be management failure and it is imperative for board members and their equivalent in non-incorporated businesses to have sound systems in place. The need to have effective health and safety systems in place is not new, but the need to have senior managers leading their businesses is, in many cases, a weak link in the command chain.

Throughout the book the authors have added 'Help Points' which will provide the reader with useful information, explanations or identifies further reading or guidance. This means that the book will provide sound advice – not just to senior management, management and supervisory staff – but to everybody at work, no matter their status or type of employment.

The authors wish to thank Tim Southam for his contribution on behavioural change – human factors and Phil Bradbury for his contribution – change control process. Special thanks to Lyn Hirst for undertaking the editing challenge.

Michael Welham and Stewart Risk
July 2004

Contents

Chapter 8: Practical Risk Management

About the Authors

Stewart Risk, BSc CEng FIMarEST

Stewart was born in Essex and, having qualified as an engineer, has worked in industry following graduation. He progressed his career to the position of Managing Director for a company with a large workforce and turnover operating in the UK and various locations around the world. As a senior manager, he has focused on health and safety as part of a corporate culture and was recognised by BP for his personal commitment and leadership in safety. He became Vice President of a large multinational company tasked with developing health and safety leadership management on a global basis. His leadership management skills are widely respected and acknowledged. He is currently CEO of Resource, an environmental business development group supported by the Scottish Enterprise and the Department of Trade and Industry.

Michael Welham, MPhil MSc FIOSH RSP FIIRSM MEWI

Michael was born in Kent and following military service worked in industry working in the UK and many parts of the world as a project 'trouble shooter'. His skills were utilised as joint expedition organiser for the Norman Croucher Peruvian Andes Expedition. Following a period with BRITOIL Plc, a major oil and gas exploration and production company, he joined the Health and Safety Executive (HSE) as an operational inspector. In addition to managing a team of inspectors, he was a member of the HSE 'Manslaughter at Work' Project Group. He has a wide experience of working with senior and middle management, supervisors and the workforce of small, medium and large undertakings. He is the author of *Tolley's Corporate Killing: A Manager's Guide to Legal Compliance*. He is a Magistrate and is leaving the HSE at the end of 2004.

It is the intention of both authors to establish a consultancy to provide practical help to companies to comply with and, preferably, exceed the expectations of health and safety law and assist with the development of safety leadership within senior management.

Selected Bibliography

Books

Adair John, Not Bosses But Leaders (2003) Kogan Page, London, ISBN 0 7494 3899 1

Commission Law, 1996, Legislating the Criminal Code – Involuntary Manslaughter, Law Com No 237-HC171, HMSO, London

Evans M, Pinto A, Corporate Criminal Liability (2003) Sweet and Maxwell, London, ISBN 0 42179280 9

Forlin Gerard, Appleby Michael, Corporate Liability – Work Related Deaths and Criminal Prosecutions (2003) Butterworths, London, ISBN 0 406 93176 3

Health & Safety Commission, Revitalising Health & Safety (2000)

Home Office, Reforming the Law on Involuntary Manslaughter: The Government's Proposals (2000)

Moore Robert, A Time to Die – The Kirsk Disaster (2003) Bantam, ISBN 0 553 81385 4

Morrell Margot, Capparell Stephanie, Shackleton's Way – Leadership Lessons from the Great Antarctic Explorer (2002) Nicholas Brealey Publishing, ISBN 1 85788 318 7

Rose Norton, Norton Rose Report on Corporate Killing – Views from Business (2004) Norton Rose, London

Slapper G, Toms S, Corporate Crime (1999) Pearson Education Ltd, ISBN 0-582-29980-2 PPR

Smith and Hogan, Criminal Law (9th edn, 1999) Butterworths, LexisNexis, London, ISBN: 0 406 98383 6

Warner Jackie, Park Fred, Requiem for a Diver (1990) Brown, Son & Ferguson, Glasgow, ISBN: 0 85174 578 4

Welham M, Corporate Killing, A Manager's Guide to Legal Compliance (2002) Butterworths Tolley LexisNexis, ISBN 0 75451 066-2

Wells Celia, Corporations and Criminal Responsibility (1994) Oxford University Press, Oxford, ISBN 0 19 825947 6

Wolmar Christian, Broken Rails; How Privatisation Wrecked Britain's Railways (2001) Aurum Press, London, ISBN 1 85410 857 3

Health and Safety Executive information

HSE, 1994, Essentials of Health & Safety at Work, ISBN 0 7176 0716 X

HSE, HSG48, Reducing Error and Influencing Behaviour, ISBN 0 7176 2452 8

HSE, HSG61, Health Surveillance at Work, ISBN 0 7176 1705 X

HSE, HSG65, Successful Health and Safety Management, ISBN 0 7176 1276

HSE, HSG137, Health Risk Management, A Practical Guide for Managers in Small and Medium Sized Enterprises, ISBN 0 7176 0905 7

HSE, HSG159, Managing Contractors – A Guide for Employers, ISBN 0 7176 1196 5

HSE, HSG218, Tackling Work Related Stress – A Manager's Guide to Improving and Maintaining Employee Health and Well Being, ISBN 0 7176 2050 6

HSE, L21, Management of Health & Safety at Work, Approved Code of Practice and Guidance, ISBN 0 7176 24889

HSE, Five Steps to Risk Assessment, INDG 163

HSE, Selecting a Health and Safety Consultancy, INDG 133

HSE, Managing Risk – Adding Value, ISBN: 0 7176 1536 7

HSE, Reducing Risk, Protecting People, ISBN 0 7176 2151 0

Health and safety publications

Safety Management, The British Safety Council, 70 Chancellors Road, London, W6 9RS

The Safety and Health Practitioner, Institution of Occupational Safety and Health, CMP Information Ltd, 245 Blackfriars Road, London, SE1 9UY

Health and Safety Bulletin, Industrial Relations Services, Tolley House, 2 Addiscombe Road, Croydon, CR9 5AF

Health and Safety at Work, Butterworth Tolley, 2 Addiscombe Road, Croydon, CR9 5AF.

Chapter 1

The Poacher and the Gamekeeper

Introduction

1.0   The title of this book, the Poacher and the Gamekeeper, came about to emphasise the safety challenges to a senior manager from industry and a government enforcer. The senior manager has been responsible for hundreds of employees and budgets of several million pounds and encompasses health and safety as a prime business function because he believes that it is of value to his business and employees as well as those who, whilst are not employed, can be affected by the business activities. The government regulator seeks compliance with health and safety law and acknowledges that a safe place of work is of value to everybody and all organisations and that there are potentially serious implications for those who fail.

The authors have worked together whilst on 'opposite sides of the fence' and both believe in the welfare of people at work and those who can be affected by workplace activities. With that in mind, they have combined their knowledge and experiences to draw together lessons learned and promote leadership management for health and safety in the workplace. Therefore, this book is of importance to everybody involved in any type of business or industry because, while it focuses on health and safety, the concepts identified apply to every aspect of any business. It must be emphasised that there is no dividing line in size, structure or location of an undertaking and it matters not what service or product is provided or manufactured. It is accepted that the risk issues for a nuclear power station cannot be compared with a telephone call centre and the workplace environment differs for a train driver when compared with a factory worker. It is also acknowledged that the hazards and subsequent risks encountered by individual undertakings can vary dramatically.

However, the need for leadership, ownership and corporate culture values are paramount. The statement made by Peter Drucker, which applies to all businesses is that the first duty of business is to survive and the guiding principle of business economics is not the maximisation of profit it is the avoidance of loss. Peter Drucker was born in 1909 in Vienna and was

1

educated there and in England and in 1927 he went to the United States. Drucker's management books and analysis of economics and society are widely read and respected throughout the world and have been translated into more than 20 languages.

Leadership in mitigating risk

1.1   Without leadership from senior management with regard to health and safety, there is no direction or motivation. That will render safety policies, statements and procedures ineffective. So in the spirit of corporate governance, mitigating corporate risk with regard to health and safety is a key issue for all directors and senior managers and needs to be addressed as an integrated part of the business culture. This requires positive leadership and as John Adair, a leading authority on leadership management, states:

> 'You can be appointed a manager but you are not a leader until your personality and character, your knowledge and your skill in doing the functions of leadership are recognised by the others involved'.

The word 'leadership' conjures up a picture that can be all things to all people and who is a leader to one person can be seen as quite the opposite to another. However, a true leader will adopt health and safety management because in a world of continuing change, risk reduction and business improvement, there needs to be positive leadership. It can be argued that there are managers but few leaders and so the question, therefore, has to be: what is a leader, what are the qualities and what are the personal attributes? The word 'leadership' carries some of the important attributes and are identified as follows.

LEADERSHIP
Lead by example
Encourage ownership
Address problems
Develop safety culture
Ensure competence
Responsibilities identified
Set standards
Help not hinder
Inform and communicate
Positive and proactive

Lead by example

1.2   Leaders lead, managers manage and there is a difference. It is the manager who leads that is the important factor. Possibly the most important of the key requirements is for management, no matter the position within the undertaking, to set an example. There is absolutely no point in having health and safety policies and procedures and expecting staff to follow them if senior management ignores or does not support them. This creates a 'one rule for us' and 'one rule for them' situation and leadership becomes non-existent.

Encourage ownership

1.3   Ownership of health and safety by staff in an undertaking has changed and one reason is that long-term permanent jobs are being lost. The problem is compounded by the situation where many workers are, for example, contractors, agency personnel, subcontractors, casual staff, etc. People arrive, do a work task and leave at the end of their allotted time and are less likely to be flexible and have little or no loyalty to the undertaking. Good leadership management can encourage ownership, to draw staff into the 'team' even when they are not direct employees.

Address problems

1.4   Senior management must address problems that arise with health, safety and welfare issues. Faced with critical problems the leader will address problems and not 'sweep them under the carpet' hoping that they go away. A leader will acknowledge that high-level responsibilities cannot be delegated and so the leader can establish control and maintain leadership and encourage staff interaction in problem solving.

Develop safety culture

1.5   A leader will ensure that as part of the corporate governance, health and safety will be integrated as part of the corporate structure and not an 'add on'. Reference is often made to a company's 'safety culture' and it is probably the most difficult environment for senior management to develop. A key objective is that there must be an environment where staff are not afraid to say 'no' or 'stop – it is not safe'. They must be able to take such action and know that they will be supported and that the leadership culture will allow it, without redress. A leader will recognise that an open culture will get staff on-board with health and safety and move away from a blame culture where management looks for a junior member of staff to 'carry the can' when there is an incident, particularly if there is 'blood on the floor'.

Ensure competence

1.6   Competence is derived from a combination of work experience and formal training. An organisation cannot flourish if members of the staff are not competent in the tasks that they are required to do. This particularly extends to health and safety advice because senior management is relying on the information that they receive and will act on. A leader will endeavour to obtain the highest level of competence in his health and safety advisor and will support the use of specialised expertise when required. In a developing area such as health and safety, a leader will acknowledge that his staff need to maintain their professional competence and encourage development.

To lead by example, senior managers should undertake safety management training.

Responsibilities identified

1.7   Senior management are responsible for health and safety within the organisation and to ensure that policies and procedures are complied with. The saying 'the buck stops at the top' is an important aspect of health and safety leadership management with regard to the workplace. A leader will have unrestricted access to health and safety advice and adopt business decisions to encompass any issues that may affect the corporate activities. The health and safety professional should only provide advice to the organisation and a leader will acknowledge that it is the responsibility of line managers to enact the requirements.

Set standards

1.8   It is a matter for the senior management at board level, or its equivalent to set the standards and determine the policies for the organisation. The standards must be the highest that the organisation can aspire to and they may be structured with milestones with realistic targets to be attained. Standards can be generated in-house or through external sources and good management will ensure that the most appropriate are identified and adopted. Leadership management, having set the objectives, will have to monitor achievement and modify the standards if required.

Help not hinder

1.9   Leadership management will adopt a style that helps and encourages staff. Senior management who micro-manage (ie get involved in the finer detail of day-to-day management) ultimately hinder a health and safety culture. A leader will be able to delegate and provide effective support when needed. Leadership management adopts careful but unobtrusive monitoring and provides effective support when required.

Inform and communicate

1.10 There is nothing worse than no information – only perhaps limited information poorly presented. Staff can generally cope with bad news, delight in good news and so it is imperative that a good leader will be able to communicate at all levels. This can involve staff and public which means that the leader is the face and personality of the organisation and being a good communicator is a very important aspect.

Positive and proactive

1.11 In business, possibly the most difficult task by senior management is to maintain a positive and proactive approach at all times. Business activities fluctuate with both positive and negative outcomes and it is for a good leader to react in a way that, in times of adversity, the leader remains positive and through proactive actions leads the team and the business to achieve successful outcomes.

It is important to identify that managers manage often by the position that they hold and the perceived or real power that they hold over subordinates. A leader does not have to invoke 'power' but can motivate all in an organisation. Good health and safety is good for business and a leadership manager is a good business motivator.

The ultimate challenge for a safety leader is to predict where the next accident could occur and put in place measures to prevent it happening.

Unlike a healthy bottom line in a profitable company, the results of good safety leadership are non-events and so a safety leader's task is never ending.

The 'Poacher'

1.12 The scene which is set in the introduction above identifies Stewart Risk as the 'poacher', a role that does not sit easily with him as he is very proactive in the whole health and safety leadership management process. As a qualified engineer he entered the offshore industry in 1976 and worked his way to become a base manager for a company in Great Yarmouth responsible for a turnover of £1m. Following a good grounding in management within a high-risk industry, he was promoted to Managing Director with a staff of over 1,000 personnel and a turnover of £150m. However, it was while attending the funeral following the death of a

21-year-old diver, an only child, which was the turning point for Stewart because he experienced the misery first hand.

It was after this incident that, as head of the company, he focused on safety, operational efficiency, customer satisfaction and quality achieving ISO 9001 accreditation and ISO 14001 accreditation for environmental management. He was particularly pleased to be recognised by BP for his personal commitment and leadership in safety.

A notable achievement for his commitment to safety involved him as senior management in the high risk and successful safe raising of the Russian nuclear submarine *Kursk*. As managing director of DSND Subsea he was involved in corporate takeovers with all the trauma that is involved and his focus was to improve DSND's safety performance allowing the company to achieve a leading position for a corporate health and safety culture. His leadership and commitment to health and safety was rewarded when, in 2001, the company won a ROSPA Gold Award for safety on first application. His vision of workplace health and safety was further rewarded when he was promoted to the position of Vice President where he managed a project to standardise worldwide procedures through a high-level business manual for the group to ensure efficient and safe operations on a global basis.

In 2002, DSND merged with Halliburton Subsea to form Subsea 7 and Stewart was made Vice President of health, safety, environment and quality with the responsibility for delivering the new company's standardised corporate processes throughout the global operations. Understanding that the organisation had systems and procedures, the next step was to review the situation to determine if they were adopted and effective. To achieve this, he conducted advanced safety audits with personnel, reviewed risk assessment processes, permit-to-work systems, subcontractor management and general site safety as well as environmental and quality systems. His leadership skills and knowledge had become a sought after commodity and he was offered a new challenge when in 2003 he became CEO of Resource, an environmental business development group supported by the Scottish Enterprise and the Department of Trade and Industry.

Extreme risk

1.13 An extreme example of workplace risk was Stewart's entry into working life when he was involved in the repairs to cracks in the walls of the fuel rod transfer duct, between the fuel rod storage pond and the reactor chamber at the United Kingdom Atomic Energy Authority's Steam Generating Heavy Water Reactor at Winfrith in Dorset. Many lessons can be learnt from the experiences of this contract and the work would not be conducted in a similar manner today, or at least we would hope not.

However, in 1977 for a young and enthusiastic diving team with little to no understanding of the risks from the nuclear products, the main consideration was that the diving conditions were excellent. This meant diving in crystal clear, warm, demineralised water with no currents; and with less than 30 feet water depth there were decompression illness issues. Prior to undertaking the diving operations, the health physics staff took extensive samples from the dive team. Risk assessments were for the future and, regrettably, the test conducted with a view to long-term safety was the amount of radiation absorbed. It was evident that not as much effort was put into protection of the divers and it was hard to determine whose safety leadership they were working under.

The problem was that the storage pond water was being lost through the cracks in the concrete walls and the work was to drill and fix steel plates onto the walls. These retained a rubber membrane and a sealant was injected between the membrane and the concrete face to seal the cracks. The divers worked with the same radiation barrier philosophy that the general plant workers operated under, which required screening for radiation at the end of each shift. They were advised of the 'safe' distance they would need to keep from the fuel rods. However, the diving equipment became contaminated during diving operations and was retained in the facility. The risk assessment process was very rudimentary and they were advised not to stir up the black sludge lying on the base of the tunnel and to monitor the situation; diving was conducted using film badges and dosimeters to record the radiation dose they picked up. One of the diving team who was young and enthusiastic dropped a spanner whilst tightening the expanding bolts. To recover it he dived to the base of the transfer tunnel to search among the sludge to locate it. The outcome was that his head became badly contaminated and when trying to decontaminate himself it was the threat of having his hair shaved off that made his efforts with a scrubbing brush more determined. Another less fortunate diver ingested a radioactive particle and became an unwilling guest of the nuclear facility until he returned the particle to the owner through his natural body process.

When working at the worksite the fuel rods hanging vertically nearby looked eerie and the water surrounding them glowed with a bluish purple colour. This was Cherenkov radiation and occurs when charged particles moving faster than the speed of light trigger off a cascade of photons which form the visible blue glow. The fact that water was very effective in absorbing radiation was reassuring and it was extremely warm which is understandable in view of the continuous pops and bangs that could be heard coming from the hot reactor chamber while underwater. The work was hard and carried out whilst sealed in what was described as an all-in-one, rubber dry diving suit which, as an industry standard, always leaked. It was very hot and the fine spray of water that entered the poorly fitting mask, which for the divers was very refreshing, however, nobody told the divers that they could not drink it.

The reactor was shut down in 1990 and a visit to the United Kingdom Atomic Energies website reveals that the reactor is now in a state of passive safety and will be held on a care and maintenance basis to allow the benefits of radioactive decay to be realised when the final stages of decommissioning are undertaken in 2023. The infamous 'sludge' will be immobilised and held in long-term storage on site.

Stewart's career evolved and, as the managing director of a major contracting company, he encountered his second nuclear risk situation. In order that the divers who intervened on the recovery of the Russian nuclear submarine, *Kursk*, were not subjected to similar laissez faire standards that he had encountered, a detailed risk assessment of all aspects of the project was undertaken involving the diving contractors, divers, scientists, submarine manufacturers and specialist munitions experts. The reactors in this case were automatically shut in when the explosion occurred and no unusual radiation levels were detected during the operation. So some things have changed throughout the years and the recovery of the *Kursk* is a classic example of a high-risk operation involving a number of contractors working together and the operation is worthy of a brief examination.

The Kursk operation

1.14   On Saturday 12 August 2000, the Russian navy submarine *Kursk* was in the Southern Barents Sea on a Russian Northern fleet exercise. The *Kursk* had come to periscope depth to launch two practise torpedoes at the *Peter the Great* cruiser. The practise torpedo to be used in the exercise was powered with a propulsion system devised in the 1920s where a conventional fuel such as kerosene is boosted by mixing it with an oxidant. Oxygen could be used but there are obvious risks in having liquid oxygen in the confines of a submarine and, instead, hydrogen peroxide was utilised.

It is an unfortunate fact and one highlighted in this book that by looking back in history, knowledge from previous incidents could have been used to reduce the risk. Certainly the risk of carrying such weapons could have been determined. In 1955, the British submarine *HMS Sidon*, while in Portland harbour suffered an explosion of a torpedo within one of the torpedo tubes. The torpedo was powered with a fuel which included the use of hydrogen peroxide. The submarine sunk and 12 of the crew were killed as a result of the explosion. When investigated it was found the damage was caused by the torpedo's fuel and not by the warhead which did not explode. Hydrogen peroxide when in contact with certain metals can give off intense heat and the Royal Navy concluded that this was too high a risk in the confines of a submarine and, after this incident, never used torpedoes with this type of fuel again.

The first explosion in the *Kursk's* torpedo room was recorded at 11:28:27. The *Kursk* sank with all its communications masts extended yet no distress signals were transmitted. Shortly after the first explosion, a second massive explosion detected by seismologists around the world occurred and the severely damaged *Kursk* came to rest on the seabed of the South Barents Sea. Of the 118 crewmembers, 23 crewmembers survived the explosions in compartments towards the stern of the submarine but further distress was caused as these crewmembers could not be rescued and also died. Attempts were made to rescue those crewmembers trapped in the submarine after the initial explosions and both specialist vessels from the Russian fleet and specialist underwater support vessels from the North Sea oil industry were contracted to intervene on the *Kursk*.

It was the morning of 8 October 2001 when the nuclear powered and armed submarine made its last journey up from the seabed. The divers and marine crew of the dynamically positioned diving support vessel *Mayo* had spent the previous three months under contract to the Dutch contractors, Mammoet and Smit, preparing the 15,000 ton vessel for lifting from the seabed. DSND Subsea Ltd provided the dynamically positioned diving support vessel DSND *Mayo* and crew to undertake the preparatory work required to recover the *Kursk* from the seabed. The major scope of work required the extensively damaged bow section to be cut from the submarine using an abrasive wire cutting system and holes to be cut into the outer and inner pressure hull of the *Kursk* to allow lifting wire attachments to be clamped into the hull.

Retaining the integrity of the two 190-megawatt nuclear reactors during the lifting of the submarine from the seabed was a prime consideration in the engineering analysis as was the risk from the 22 Granit cruise missiles housed in their silos in the submarines hull. The nuclear risk was controlled through a Radiation Control Zone checklist. In addition to these obvious risks during the lifting operation, an extremely comprehensive identification, analysis and mitigation of the risks to the divers and support crew of the dynamically positioned diving support vessel DSND *Mayo* was conducted.

The risks were extensive and excellent co-operation was experienced from the many specialists required to identify and quantify the risks. The submarine designers, Rubens, were extremely co-operative from the outset. Nuclear experts were brought in to assist with an analysis of the nuclear risk and, in addition, weapons experts were also consulted to determine the risk from possible unexploded ordnance in the bow section.

The 26 holes of around 700 mm diameter cut through both inner and outer hulls involved cutting through many service lines, the contents of which all had to be determined to ensure they would not cause harm to the diving teams. Accessing the steel hull required the removal of the acoustic tiles and the composition of these tiles had to be determined to ensure the divers would not be contaminated during the cutting operations.

To reassure the divers that there was no nuclear risk to them, extensive monitoring equipment was installed at the work sites. After discussion with the scientists involved in the recovery programme and with input from DSND's management, who had experience of diving in a nuclear reactor fuel rod storage pond, it was agreed a barrier system would be used similar to that adopted when working in nuclear plants. This required all personal equipment that could have become contaminated to be retained outside the divers' living chambers and other non-personal equipment that could be contaminated was stored for return to the surface where a similar barrier system was adopted by the deck crew to isolate any sources of contamination. Both reactors had automatically shut down and at no time were radiation levels detected which were above normal background radiation levels.

To undertake the initial hazard identification and assessment, a hotel conference room in Aberdeen was utilised to accommodate the numbers of specialists required to undertake this initial activity. Some of the underwater activities required extensive engineering analysis and included, for example, an analysis of the vibrations induced in the submarine's hull during the wire rope cutting operations to separate the damaged bow section to ensure that no further explosions would occur. Also, an analysis of the submarine's service and control lines that were being cut while making the holes in the hull was made to ensure there would be no uncontrolled release of any of the cruise missiles onboard as a result of the cables being severed. The risk assessments were comprehensive and proved to be so as there were very few issues raised offshore. The experts from various disciplines was a key factor in the operation and both Wally Wallace and Shaun Pople, the on-site diving project managers, were strong leaders, both quiet and unassuming.

All of these preparations paid dividends and with the extensive effort made from the outset, the only injury recorded was to one of the diver's eardrums which occurred during one of the cutting operations which, whilst disappointing that anyone should suffer an injury, was a credit to all of the diving crew, scientists, engineers, technicians and mariners involved in the operation.

Subsequent to the successful raising of the *Kursk*, a presentation on the recovery operation was given to a group of oil industry personnel. After the presentation, an engineer from an oil company commented to the presenter that it probably was not necessary to assess the risk of an accidental launch of a cruise missile. The response from the speaker was that no missiles have been accidentally launched during the operation and safety was all about preventing undesired events.

The 'Gamekeeper'

1.15 Following military service as a diver, Mike Welham was employed by commercial diving companies where he held a variety of positions including saturation diver, project superintendent to project 'trouble shooter' operating in the UK, Norway, Brazil, Middle East, Mediterranean and West Africa. The accumulated professional knowledge and experience found him headhunted into a major oil exploration and production company, Britoil Plc (to later merge with BP), for five years. His work involved offshore operations and onshore management functions that included the co-ordination of daily running, future planning of the department's operations including emergency procedures, safety audits and oil pollution controls to ensure compliance with codes of safe practice, procedures and legislation on all matters relating to diving personnel, diving systems and diving support vessels (DSVs) in support of construction, inspection and remedial work.

Using his professional knowledge he portrayed the underwater world of work, in his book, *Exploring the Deep* (Patrick Stephens Ltd, 1994), which includes chapters on all aspects of commercial diving, the use of underwater vehicles and dynamically positioned vessels with text, accompanied by a myriad of photographs. His time with Britoil was a culture change and gave him the foundation of corporate risk management. This focused on the business of commercial targets balanced against health and safety factors both in-house and with contractors. Throughout this period he had interfaced with the Health and Safety Executive diving inspectors to develop an understanding of the law and its impact on the industry. The focus of utilising his knowledge and experience in health and safety was to be of value when he became of an inspector with the Department of Energy and subsequently the Health and Safety Executive (HSE).

As a principal inspector with the HSE he manages a team of inspectors tasked with the enforcement of health and safety legislation, site inspections, corporate audits, accident investigation and enforcement action including the issue of notices and undertaking prosecutions. The team is also tasked with the review of safety cases for organisational safety management systems, major hazards and emergency response and procedures. In addition to commercial diving, he led his team as focal point for an offshore operator with a number of gas production installations and a drilling contractor. It was a period of intense work at the height of a safety case assessment process and, for the team, it meant additional training in such topics as drilling and process procedures.

While much of Mike's work has been reactive, he is passionate about the subject of workplace health and safety and extends his practical knowledge and experiences through presenting papers at numerous venues on topics relating to health and safety and many of these talks are undertaken outside of work time. A firm favourite is to focus on the specific requirements of corporate workshops where he provides a positive health and safety message and active participation.

Working with Stewart Risk, it was apparent that senior management leadership could influence a health and safety culture and it was in leadership management, the subject of a paper he presented at the Institution of Occupational Health and Safety (IOSH) National Safety Symposium 2003 which will be developed at the Anglia South District Seminar in 2004. The IOSH magazine, *Safety Practitioner*, produced a conference summary under the heading: Leadership and the Law.

> 'Legal issues were clearly in focus on the final morning of this year's Symposium with presentations by Mike Welham, HM Principal Inspector with the Health and Safety Executive. Mike, a Fellow of IOSH, took as his theme "Leadership in health and safety", arguing that without leadership from the top with regard to OSH change and developments, there is no motivation. The parliamentary system, he said, was not leading in change and pointed out that the move to introduce new or modified legislation is subject to the members 'ten-minute rule', which may mean it could be lost.'

He spoke of management failure in the context of major disasters and directors' responsibilities with regard to the the Health and Safety Commission's (HSC) 'Revitalising Health and Safety' strategy. 'The HSC recommends that boards appoint one of their number to be health and safety director', he said. He spoke of Home Secretary David Blunkett's announcement of the introduction of a new offence of corporate manslaughter and expressed the hope that it would be in the Queen's Speech this autumn. He stated:

> 'However, I hope that if we get this offence in, we never use it, because then everyone would be doing their job. Management has to lead and be seen to lead and demonstrate a commitment to safety. Good leadership will lead on health and safety ... Good leadership will encompass trust and ownership, and good leadership will show real commitment to safety and health. We need

corporate leaders, not just bosses. And to support that leadership we need effective legislation'.

Mike's occupational health and safety legal experience has been beneficial in the management of the investigation and legal process through the high court of a prosecution for individual manslaughter, perverting the course of justice, a 'section 7' offence under the Health and Safety at Work etc Act 1974 (HSWA 1974) and a company prosecuted of two counts under the HSWA 1974. The knowledge gained from this was of use when be became a member of the HSE Operations Management Forum 'Manslaughter at Work' project. At the time of writing, he and members of his team are involved in another workplace manslaughter prosecution. His expertise as a prosecutor in the Magistrates' Courts was put to use mentoring HSE inspectors in preparing and presenting prosecution cases in the Magistrates' Court. It was his managing of an investigation and evidence collection of a joint HSE, police and Crown Prosecution Service case for a potential corporate and individual manslaughter prosecution role as an expert witness for criminal courts, coroners courts and overseas civil claims in support of fatal incidents. This all provided the catalyst for his book, *Tolley's Corporate Killing: A Manager's Guide to Legal Compliance*. His knowledge and expertise of the legal process is further enhanced through being a Justice of the Peace at Norwich Magistrates' Court.

➢ **Help Point**: Michael Welham is the author of *Health Survey of Commercial Divers (A Preliminary Study)* (MaTSU P3204, 1995, HSE, London) and *Tolley's Corporate Killing: A Manager's Guide to Legal Compliance* (Butterworths Tolley LexisNexis, 2002) ISBN 0 75451 066-2.

Management failure

1.16   The failure evolving from not having safety systems or procedures exposed employees to risk and an example of this occurred in the early 70s when Mike was employed on a project in the North Sea where it required devices to be fitted to the underwater structure of a gas platform. It was a task that required him to locate the device into position and then close the two clamps and tighten the bolts. The problem was that the divers were using self-contained breathing apparatus, the same as worn today by recreational divers. The new diving equipment arrived offshore along with the diving team when it was found that that the demand-breathing valve just required a push fit to secure it. When purchasing the equipment nobody checked to see that it was fit for the purpose. There was no training or familiarisation, it was a case of 'that's the equipment – get on with it'. At the work site there were no risk assessments or project plans, no emergency procedures and the only means of escape was to emerge into the swell and climb, fully equipped for diving, up a vertical ladder to safety.

To undertake the work, a large spanner was used and so as not to lose it, a polypropylene line was attached to the spanner and the other end had a loop, which pulled tightly on the lower arm. Having pulled the spanner to its furthest point it required some movement to release it. However, in this instance on trying to remove the spanner from the anode, the demand valve became disconnected from the air cylinders. This resulted in Mike being trapped by a piece of strong line and a spanner that would not move and without any air to breathe. It was a potentially fatal situation. The willpower to survive the event enabled him to break the line and swim to the surface. The reaction of management was to complain about the cost of the lost 'special' demand valve which had been pulled from his mouth as he ascended, and to determine whether the spanner had been lost. There was not one question as to the well being of Mike and it transpired that the 'new' underwater breathing equipment was, in fact, only certified as being suitable for firefighting and not for use underwater.

Human failings

1.17   Deployed out of the diving bell on the 10 August 1980 to work at 510 feet (140 metres) below the surface of the North Sea, Mike knew that it was to be some 12 hours before they were recovered and returned to the chambers located on the surface vessel. Whilst he was out working on a flow-line connection, the second diver supporting him remained inside the bell and would only enter the water to change over with Mike or to go to his aid in an emergency. After a period of eight hours, Mike returned to change over so that the second diver could continue with the task. Having left the diving bell and made his way to the worksite it was not long before it became apparent that the other diver was not going to be able to complete the work. Mike was asked to go back out and finish the connections so the line could be pressure tested. Mike returned to the seabed for another 3½ hours until the task was eventually completed and it was time for Mike to return to the diving bell.

Wearing diving equipment and a suit full of hot water did not make for an easy and rapid access into the bell. Having climbed up and inside he sat down to remove his band mask. He was breathing heavily from the exertion of work and getting into the bell and as the mask came away from his face it was within seconds that he knew something was wrong. He could not breathe and was in the process of blacking out but managed to tell the supervisor at the surface that he was unwell. In those few seconds he knew that he had not had any problems breathing from the mask and as his head fell forward, he pushed the mask up into his face. As he struggled for breath it became easier and he rapidly began to feel better and was able to inform the supervisor at the surface that the atmosphere in the bell was contaminated. He directed the other diver, who was also feeling unwell, to open the pressurisation valve. Doing so, a mixture of helium and oxygen gas flowed into the bell pushing the contaminated gas out of the bottom into the water to be dispersed in a mass of bubbles.

There is no doubt that it had been a very close thing and the cause was one of human failure. The bell has a carbon dioxide scrubber inside to keep the atmosphere breathable but the other diver had knocked the control lever and caused the scrubber to be turned off, leaving the diver to sit inside the bell. Because he was not moving he was breathing shallow, but was very slowly replacing the atmosphere with lethal carbon dioxide. The exertion of getting Mike's umbilical into the bell and him climbing up inside had rapidly changed the atmosphere to one that would not support life.

The failings were that the diver had not realised that the scrubber was not making a noise; the diving supervisor could hear the unit when it was running through the communication system but failed to note that it was not working and the supervisor had failed to test the bell atmosphere. These were simple failures that could have caused loss of life and it was to be Mike's last commercial bell dive. Today the incident would have to be reported to the HSE but at that time such events were not reported, even though a limited number of diving specialist inspectors were employed by the Department of Energy.

'Official' leadership

1.18 Prior to the incident above that Mike was involved with and as an outcome of the growing number of fatal incidents, the Government of the day established a unique department under the leadership of Commander Jackie Warner to police offshore diving operations. This regime was extremely prescriptive and, for the most part, reactive to incidents but safety was improved as a result of Commander Warner's leadership. To administer this new legislation, Commander Warner, as a civilian, became the first diving inspector in 1974 as part of the newly formed Department of Energy Diving Inspectorate. His endeavours are described in a forthright manner in his book, *Requiem for a Diver* (Brown, Son & Ferguson, 1990). One of his first and most important tasks was to issue a Diving Safety Memorandum (DSM) from the Department of Energy to the offshore industry. The document was not legally binding but, like those that have followed, it provided a basis for industry standards. The memorandum clearly points out his concern that diving supervisors were being placed in untenable situations and that divers' lives were being put at risk. This was a clear warning to those who applied the pressure that they could be in breach of the new Regulations. The DSM is quoted in full:

> 'The Offshore Installations (Diving Operations) Regulations 1974 place considerable responsibility for safe conduct of diving operations on the diving supervisor and, indeed, the diver himself.
>
> There is no doubt that, at all times, everybody involved in offshore exploration for minerals are under considerable pressure due to the vast amount of money invested. However, this situation must not be allowed to put unnecessary pressure on diving supervisors to continue operations when they consider that conditions are unsuitable. Diving companies are requested to report to the Inspector of Diving any occasion when, in their opinion or in the opinion of the diving supervisor, undue pressure has been brought to bear to carry out diving operations which are beyond the normally accepted safe diving practices.'

This situation was laudable in that it offered an escape route for companies and supervisors under pressure but, in reality, nobody was going to stand up and point the finger. Any company that did would find that it was no longer asked to bid for work and diving supervisors who made a complaint would, in effect, find themselves unemployable. The only way that companies or individuals were taken to task or prosecuted was as a result of an accident where divers were seriously injured or killed and those prosecutions were not always successful.

The Infabco incident

1.19   Commercial diving was one of the highest risk occupations with statistically the highest national death rate. Risk management was personal and a matter for the teams to confront pressures to undertake unsafe practices. The corporate line was generally motivated by profit but after the Infabco incident there was a sea of change. The most dramatic diving incident occurred in the summer of 1979 and was to change the diving industry in the North Sea and be the springboard for specific diving safety regulations. Details of the incident are taken from an official Fatal Accident Inquiry held in Aberdeen and involved a diving contractor, Infabco Diving Services Ltd, who were employed by the British National Oil Corporation Ltd (BNOC) to carry out diving work at one of their installations. The diving support vessel chartered by Infabco with which to undertake the work was the *MV Wildrake*.

The whole incident was based upon a travesty of errors and failures which resulted in the death of two divers. On 7 August 1979 at about 11.00 pm, two divers were lowered in the *Wildrake's* diving bell to about 485 feet

(148 metres). One diver was locked out of the bell and was using a hand-held video camera to film the subsea structure. The diving supervisor, in the dive control van, heard a bang and saw the lift wire of the main diving bell jump, followed by the diver in the bell declaring that the main lift wire had parted. The supervisor directed the diver to take the camera to the bell so that he could see what had happened. On the monitor in the dive control the supervisor could see that the bell was hanging at an angle of some 45 degrees. This indicated that the bell was in fact hanging on the main umbilical which carried all of the life support services to the bell. The supervisor instructed the diver to get back in the bell, close the inside door and pressure it up, so that the pressure was greater inside the bell than the surrounding water pressure and both divers would be in a safe environment and could be rescued. At this point, the supervisor lost communications with the bell and was unaware of what had happened to the main lift wire. (It was established that the pin which held the connection between the lifting wire and the diving bell had come out. There was no explanation as to how this occurred.)

The only means of recovery available to them was the umbilical and that had jammed in the winch sheave and was itself damaged. With the two primary life support functions in a critical state, they could not monitor the well being of the divers and with the loss of hot water they would be subjected to hypothermia. The supervisor remained in the dive control and continued to attempt communicating with the bell, and did so for about an hour. The reception was extremely poor and the only message deciphered was that the bell should be lowered to the seabed. That was to be the last communication with the divers.

Another diving support vessel, the *Stena Welder*, was in the area and it was called to assist and effect a rescue. The plan, which was formulated for the rescue, was for the *Stena Welder's* divers to locate the lost bell and attach a guide wire to it. The *Wildrake's* crane wire would then be sent down it and the divers would connect it to the bell. Due to other factors, ie the *Stena Welder's* bell had, in fact, been out of use due to repairs and maintenance, it was not fully functional when employed to undertake the rescue. Eventually, the *Stena Welder's* divers were able to dive and located the lost bell and made the connection to the *Wildrake* crane.

The crane driver was instructed to begin the lift and, after a short period of time, it was noticed that the crane wire was not vertical but running at an angle. Then the crane driver reported that he had a very heavy strain on the wire and was instructed to slew the crane boom from side to side. This he did, and when the weight was no longer on the wire he recovered it. At the surface there was no bell, just a broken wire. What had happened was that the wire had been fouled on the subsea structure, which meant that the bell could not be pulled free. Divers from the *Stena Welder* were committed to the water again and continued in the attempt to attach a cable to the bell. Eventually, the wire was connected and the bell lifted to the surface, and locked onto the *Wildrake's* chambers. A doctor confirmed that both divers were dead and that the cause of death was hypothermia.

The company was prosecuted and at trial in the Aberdeen Sheriff Court it was held that because the divers were not employees of the company, there was no basis for a criminal prosecution against the company. It was a shock to the regulators and the families of the deceased and it is beyond the scope of this book to examine the failure of the prosecution. Suffice to say that a serious loophole in the legal system was blocked so that any future incident would ensure that the employers would be liable to prosecution for health and safety failures.

Lessons not learned

1.20   There are two key factors that arise in all industries:

• 　　a lack of corporate memory; and

• 　　not learning from serious incidents.

This means that serious incidents are repeated – often with loss of life. For example, even in the relatively small industry of commercial diving death often comes from the most basic safety failure.

The first case occurred many years ago when divers were working on a pipeline, which had been laid to connect an offshore installation to an onshore terminal. The pipeline was laid full of air to reduce the weight transmitted to the lay barge which was on the surface installing the pipe. After laying the pipe, a diver was working in close proximity to the seaward end of the pipeline when a valve was actuated at the shore end of the pipeline, which causes the pipeline to flood with water. The water, under considerable pressure, poured into the pipe at the seaward end causing the diver to be sucked into the pipe where he was tragically killed. Not aware of the risk to divers on the seabed or the situation, the surface crew deployed the standby diver who was also sucked into the pipeline and killed. Still unaware of the problem below, a third diver was made ready and deployed. He was also sucked into the pipe but because the pipeline was almost equalised he was able to extricate himself and avoid being killed.

A workforce which is trained in basic risk management will have a better chance of avoiding injury and management must ensure and has an obligation to ensure that its workforce has adequate training. However, in

December 2002, there was a diving fatality which, in this case, occurred in West Africa. The accident happened during the installation of a 58 cm flexible hose, 40 metres long, between a seabed manifold and a new surface-loading buoy in a water depth of 35 metres. Prior to the installation of the flexible hose, a solid wooden plate (10 mm thick) was placed across the flange at the bottom end of the hose to protect the O-rings from damage. This plate was not part of the original hose installation procedure and was added on site.

The flexible hose was then pulled down to the manifold by a cable and winch which was located on the buoy. At about 13 metres water depth the hose stopped due to the buoyancy forces in the flexible hose which had not flooded due to the sealing effect of the wooden plate. It was evident that the plate had to be removed and rather than recover the hose to the surface to remove it, a diver tried to remove the plate with his knife but, because of the high suction forces involved, he broke the knife. It was estimated that the force holding on the wooden plate was some two tonnes. Unable to lever the plate away, he took the broken knife blade and with a hammer, drove the blade into the plate. At this stage there was a loss of communication with the diver combined with a fast payout of his life support umbilical. The umbilical went slack and was recovered to the surface along with the divers soft hood, complete with a front faceplate, oral nasal air supply but without the video camera. Also attached to the equipment was part of the wooden plate. The stand-by diver was deployed and after a short period of time the diver was located. He had suffered massive head injuries and had been killed as a result of the incident. The accident occurred when the wooden plate broke which allowed a sudden severe flooding of the flexible hose causing the diver to be sucked into the pipe end.

Although this diving operation was undertaken overseas, the operation was being conducted to UK standards and following the International Maritime Contractors Association (IMCA) diving guidance and procedures. In this case, the cause of the incident was human error resulting from a lack of planning/procedures, poor supervision and a lack of awareness of the potential risks. The dive team was made up of personnel who were more used to salvage diving and the question has to be asked if this was a factor in the incident in that are these divers are more inclined to be 'risk takers' as opposed to 'offshore' divers who are governed more strictly by regulations and rules?

The investigation found that there was:

• a lack of adequate supervision and general co-ordination;

- a disregard of the client's work specifications, IMCA rules and the diving contractor's own manuals;

- a poor diving plan which was not backed-up by risk assessment;

- a lack of management of change procedures in respect of the operating procedures;

- a lack of any pre-dive safety talk or instructions and a poorly designed solution, such as the wooden plate having a hole in it to equalize pressures.

There were other contributory factors, which included:

- poor safety awareness;

- considerable pressure to get the job finished on time; and

- an inadequate sized team.

The examples illustrated above have been drawn from one particular industry, that of commercial diving only because it was relevant to the authors' background, but the failures apply to all industries and businesses. They are generally management failures in that they may fail to provide adequate procedures, equipment, training, supervision or resources. There is, of course, one major key factor – and that is the human element where those doing the job ignore all safety provisions and take risks because their understanding and perception of risk are very different from those looking out for their well being. Safety leaders will encompass all of these issues and will have encouraged a robust health and safety culture where people think before they act.

Chapter Two

The Outcome of Management Failure

Introduction

2.0   There have been significant management failures with regard to health and safety resulting in some very serious incidents and, in some cases, what are described as disasters. It is not the purpose of this book to examine every one of these failures, but within the book there will be a focus on some of those where investigations and enquiries have identified and highlighted management failure with regard to health and safety.

Among the failures that are documented is the report of the Public Inquiry for investigations into the Piper Alpha disaster by Lord Cullen who stated:

> 'I am convinced from the evidence ... that the quality of safety management by operators is fundamental to offshore safety. No amount of detailed regulations for safety improvements could make up for deficiencies in the way that safety is managed by operators'.

In the *Herald of Free Enterprise* ferry disaster, which cost 197 lives when it sailed with the bow doors open and capsized, it was established that there had been previous incidents which identified the possibility of this unsafe situation but no action was taken by management. There was no information display or even a single warning light to tell the captain if the bow doors were open. Two years earlier, the captain of a similar vessel owned by the same company had requested that a warning light should be installed following a similar incident when he had gone to sea with his bow doors open. Company management had treated the request with derision. Following the loss of the *Herald of Free Enterprise*, bow door lights were made mandatory on roll-on, roll-off car ferries.

The message was clear when Mr Justice Sheen in the investigation report of the incident stated:

> 'a full investigation into circumstances of the disaster lead inexorably to the conclusion that the underlying or cardinal faults lay far higher up in the company ... From top to bottom the body corporate was infected with the disease of sloppiness'.

Rail disasters were to figure high in the disaster league and an examination of the incidents always brings us back to management failures. The Ladbroke disaster occurred on 5 October 1999. 31 people died and 425 were injured when an inexperienced Thames train driver passed through a red light and entered a line where he should not have been. The result was a head-on collision with a Great Western high speed train. In his book, *Broken Rails* (Aurum Press, 2002), Christian Wolmar identifies a serious failing in the communication between two key players, namely, Railtrack and Great Western, and explains:

> '... Alison Foster, First Great Western's director of operations and safety. She persistently expressed concerns over the series of SPAD's [signals passed at danger] in the Paddington area in a series of letters and tried to get Railtrack to do something about them ... She spoke of meetings where lots of ideas were generated but no follow-up was instigated ... many of her letters were simply ignored ... she wrote ... if you would advise me as a matter of urgency what action you intend to mitigate against this high risk signal [SN 109] "... I have never received a full response to that ..." The organisation does not look very often at some of the big-picture issues. They tend to be reactive to incidents and single-issue problem solving process ... and sometimes not taking a broad risk based approach to the management of safety, which I do not think is helpful for long-term improvements that we need to see ... they do not seem to be a learning organisation'.

The evidence shows that Ms Foster was dealt with as Railtrack would have dealt with any customer making a complaint – a fob-off by the customer liaison department to whom any letter of complaint would be sent, no matter who it was addressed to. The staff employed to deal with customer complaints would not recognise the importance of a letter's contents; their task was to send out a standard reply letter. This is a situation where the contractors, one with responsibility for train operations and one for infrastructure, with a shared responsibility failed on the part of one of the parties to co-operate. The result in this case was a disaster resulting in considerable loss of life and people injured. The railways were previously operated under one clearly defined entity and the change to a privatised industry was not well managed.

The catalogue of disasters

2.1   There were a number of disasters encompassed within a four-year period from 1985 to 1989 that really focused the public's attention on the total lack of corporate liability for deaths caused by the failures of directors to manage safely.

The first incident occurred in 1985 when 49 people died in the Bradford City football stadium fire. In 1987 there were two tragedies, one of which, the *Herald of Free Enterprise*, pushed the failings in corporate liability to the forefront of public attention. The *Herald of Free Enterprise* had sailed from Zeebrugge harbour with its bow doors open allowing the sea to swamp the car deck causing the vessel to capsize, resulting in 154 passengers and 38 crew being killed. The company, P&O European Ferries (Dover) Ltd, was charged with corporate manslaughter, but the case was dismissed.

In the second 1987 tragedy, 31 people died and 60 were injured when fire engulfed Kings Cross underground station. The following year, there were again two major tragedies. The first, was the Clapham train crash, which killed 37 and injured 500 people: in the same year, an explosion destroyed the *Piper Alpha* oil platform causing the deaths of 167 crew members. In 1989 there were three tragedies: the Purley train crash caused the deaths of 5 and injuries to 88 passengers, the dredger, *Bowbelle*, collision with the River Thames pleasure craft, *The Marchioness*, caused the deaths of 51 and injuries to 80 passengers, and the Hillsborough football stadium disaster caused the deaths of 95 and injuries to hundreds of spectators.

More recently, the major rail disasters have included the Southall train crash (1997) where 7 passengers were killed and 147 injured and the Paddington train crash (1999) where 31 passengers were killed and 250 injured. Of all these 'major' disasters only the *Herald of Free Enterprise* case was progressed to a corporate manslaughter prosecution and was dismissed. In the case of the Paddington (Ladbroke Grove) crash, immunity to prosecution was given to those who provided evidence, which means that the Crown Prosecution Service cannot pursue corporate manslaughter charges.

More recent incidents have included the Hatfield rail disaster where six men and the two companies have been charged with manslaughter due to gross negligence and an offence under the Health & Safety at Work etc Act 1974. Those charged with manslaughter were the director of the London North East Zone of Railtrack; the area asset manager of the London North East Zone (South) of Railtrack; the regional director until August 11, 2000 of Balfour Beatty; a civil engineer for Balfour Beatty and a track engineer of the London North Eastern Zone of Railtrack. On 28 April 2004, a report in the *Financial Times* stated that Network Rail and Jarvis (the rail maintenance company) formally accepted liability on behalf of the rail industry for claims arising from the fatal Potters Bar rail crash. By accepting liability, it did not mean that Jarvis were accepting responsibility.

The Piper Alpha disaster

2.2   In July 1988, the fire and explosions on Occidental's *Piper Alpha* platform, 120 miles north east of Aberdeen, resulted in the world's worst offshore oil disaster, claiming 167 lives. At about 10.00 pm on 6 July 1988, an explosion occurred in the gas compression module on the *Piper Alpha* platform, 176 km north east of Aberdeen. This initial explosion put the main control room and main power supplies out of action and caused extensive damage to hydrocarbon processing equipment. It was followed immediately by a large fire in the oil separation module, which gave rise to a massive plume of black smoke that engulfed the north end of the platform. This fire was fed by oil from the platform and a leak in the main oil line to the shore, to which the pipelines from two other platforms were connected.

At about 10.10 pm there was a second major explosion which caused a massive intensification of the fire. This was due to the rupture of the riser on the gas pipeline from one of the adjacent platforms. Ruptures of other risers further intensified the fire. The emergency systems failed. The platform structure collapsed as a result of the explosions. The east quarter's module lost its structural support and tipped to the west, crushing the west quarter's module, and then tipped northwards into the sea. Between 10:30 pm and 12:15 am the centre of the platform collapsed. The risers from the gas pipelines and the main oil pipeline were torn apart. The north side of the platform slowly collapsed until the additional accommodation module slipped into the water. There were 226 men on the platform at the time. The system for control in the event of an emergency was rendered almost entirely inoperative and smoke and flames outside the accommodation made evacuation by helicopter or lifeboat impossible. A number of personnel reached the sea by use of ropes and hoses or by jumping off the platform at various levels. 61 persons survived; 167 died.

The extent of death and injury resulting from the *Piper Alpha* disaster was of great concern to the offshore petroleum industry worldwide, and widespread reviews for safety equipment and emergency response were undertaken. In the UK, a public enquiry, undertaken by Lord Cullen, was commissioned in July 1988 to establish the circumstances of the accident. An outcome of the Cullen Report, which examined the causes of the disaster, was for the UK Government to establish a discrete division within the Health & Safety Executive (HSE). The HSE has responsibility for the regulating of the UK offshore oil and gas industry. The foundation of the HSE's regulating approach to the management of risk was based upon Safety Cases that were required for all fixed and mobile installations operating in the UK sector. Occidental, before the *Piper Alpha* disaster, was not a company with a good safety record and the company had narrowly escaped a disaster in 1984, which had required the mass evacuation of the platform. In 1987, the company experienced a fatal incident. The company had clearly failed to learn from its mistakes and that was made clear by Lord Cullen, whose *Piper Alpha* Inquiry concluded that there were 'significant flaws in Occidental's management of safety' and that 'senior management were too easily satisfied' and 'relied on the absence of any feedback of problems as indicating that all was well'. The facts that derived from the report indicate that, in the case of *Piper Alpha*, it was not a case of individual negligent workers, but with a corporation for which safety was relegated below that of profits. Numerous commentators argued that with the climate of profit before safety a *Piper Alpha* disaster was inevitable and could have occurred on many other North Sea platforms.

Prior to the incident, a sector-wide set of regulations and laws were applied to all platforms and were enforced by governmental inspection. This policy did not allow for customisation of safety regulations to a particular type of platform. Because of the numerous types of offshore platforms, this type of system was found to be inadequate for the North Sea production area. Subsequent to *Piper Alpha*, operators must produce a formal safety case to be approved by the regulatory body, the Offshore Safety Division of the HSE. In the formal safety case, the operator must have procedures in place to control risks to personnel and demonstrate that the current safety management is adequate. In addition to the formal safety case, a temporary refuge, typically, the accommodation unit, must exist and provide at least two hours of protection for the workers. Other factors include a Permit-to-Work-system, fire walls, deluge systems, safety training, auditing and risk assessment.

Occidental escaped enforcement action in the courts because the authorities concluded that there was insufficient evidence to proceed with a prosecution. The question that has evolved from this is to ask if economic considerations to maintain business, means that a corporation is absolved from criminal legal repercussions. The other consideration is to pass the blame onto individuals. While no official prosecution was taken, a private criminal prosecution by victims' families was an option but could not be pursued because of the legal costs involved.

Piper Alpha was the ultimate and most costly management failure in the UK offshore oil industry and one that changed the legislative structure of the industry. In the early 1980s, an individual landing by helicopter on *Piper Alpha* was immediately aware that this was a platform producing large amounts of oil and gas, the flare would be roaring and the whole structure vibrated as oil gushed through the marine riser to the subsea export pipeline carrying the oil back to shore. Prior to the disaster, *Piper*

Alpha was the most prolific oil producing platforms in the North Sea. It is interesting to note that the subsea industry was maturing in its approach to safety and when air diving in the vicinity of water intakes on *Piper Alpha*, there was a requirement to have them isolated so that the divers were not sucked into the intakes. It transpired that this was considered a contributory failure in the disaster, as over time and regardless of the location of the diver, the need to isolate intakes required the isolation of the pumps as a matter of course and hence the emergency fire pumps were isolated at the time of the first explosion. This was a tragic human disaster and, in the days following the explosions when the multi-role support vessel, the *Tharos*, was being used to support Red Adair's activities to kill the remaining fires emanating from the damaged conductors, it was a chilling experience to stand on the remains of the platform and witness first hand the scene of devastation which cost so many lives.

➢ **Help Point:** The Piper Alpha incident had a dramatic impact upon the public who saw management failures with no legal redress. Today, management of all undertakings can examine the management issues in the Cullen Report and compare with their own activities so as to learn from the failures of others.

The Herald of Free Enterprise ferry case

2.3   The first of a line of disasters that proceeded to court for manslaughter prosecutions and failed, focussed the minds of the public on the very serious failings of the UK justice system. The case in question was *R v P&O European Ferries (Dover) Ltd (1991) 93 Cr App R 72*. Here was a corporation being prosecuted for its management failings, but the Crown Prosecution Service failed to obtain a conviction. It was a case of the corporate entity placing the blame on junior employees and, because of the inability to identify a controlling mind (which was a requirement of the law prior to the proposed current legislation on corporate killing), this case was destined to fail. It was a case where the public saw a corporation that failed to adopt safe practices and procedures and held not to be accountable at director level. The public found that outcome unacceptable and, as a result of numerous lobby groups, has placed pressure on the Government to change the law.

The corporate manslaughter case of the capsizing of the *MV Herald of Free Enterprise* in the Report of the Court No 8074, 1987, Department of Transport, otherwise known as the Sheen Report, is reviewed to provide the facts of this important case and draw out the failings of the corporate body.

'The *Herald of Free Enterprise* was built for the Dover-Calais run and incorporated very powerful engines enabling the vessel to accelerate rapidly and allowing the crossing to be made at high speed. The concept of the vessel and her sister vessels, was to be able to disembark their passengers and vehicles rapidly and then, without any delay, embark passengers and vehicles for the return voyage. This is, of course, done to ensure efficiency and cost benefit.

When the vessel was transferred to the Dover to Zeebrugge route, the passage took 4½ hours, and because it is a longer journey than that of the Dover to Calais route, it gives the officers more time to relax during the transit period. On this basis, the company only employed a master and two deck officers, which they were quite entitled to do, providing proper thought had been given to the organisation of the officers' duties and the safety of all those onboard. At Zeebrugge, the turn-round was different from the turn-round at Calais in four main respects:

- only two deck officers were available;
- only one deck could be loaded at a time;
- it was frequently necessary to trim the ship by the head;
- the bow doors could be closed at the berth.

There were more officers on the Calais run which meant that immediately loading was complete the Chief Officer considered himself under pressure to leave the loading deck to go to his harbour station on the bridge.'

➢ **Help Point:** It is very evident that management failed to identify a level of manning that would combine efficiency, cost effectiveness and safety. This means that the crew size was, in part, economically driven and that the risk derived from a reduced crew was not assessed. These issues were those of management decisions and were a major contribution to the events that led to the disaster.

The report identified that there were three crews and five sets of officers for the manning of the *Herald* on this route, and that meant that the officers did not always have the same crew. There was a failing in the operating system because a competent superintendent, applying his mind to the organisation of the officers and crew, would have issued corporate adopted instructions, known within the company as 'Company Standing Orders', which would have been uniform for all the ships of one class. They would have covered all aspects of organisation, not only for the Calais run, but also for the Zeebrugge run when the ship carried only two deck officers in addition to the master. This approach in management is fundamental, however, no company orders were issued. While there were no company orders issued there were Ship's Standing Orders which were in place in March 1987 and they highlight that there was a lack of proper organisation.

➢ **Help Point**: This is vital evidence as the failure to manage the vessel was identified and this should have been a responsibility of the board members, not the master and not the ship's officers. Senior management sets the policy and has the responsibility to monitor that it is being complied with. This was not part of the corporate culture.

On 6 March 1997, the *Herald of Free Enterprise*, under the command of Captain David Lewry, sailed from Number 12 berth in the inner harbour at Zeebrugge. The ship was manned by a crew of 80 hands and was laden with 81 cars, 47 freight vehicles and 3 other vehicles. Approximately 459 passengers had embarked for the voyage to Dover. Because of the route, senior management had decided that the officer compliment would be reduced. There was prevailing good weather with a light easterly breeze and very little sea or swell. The *Herald* passed the outer mole at 18.24 hrs and capsized about 4 minutes later. During the final moments, the *Herald* turned rapidly to starboard and was prevented from sinking totally by reason that her portside rested on the bottom in shallow water. Water rapidly filled the ship below the surface level with the result that 150 passengers and 38 members of the crew lost their lives and many others were injured.

Responsibilities

2.4   The assistant bosun accepted that it was his duty to close the bow doors at the time of departure from Zeebrugge and that he failed to undertake this duty. He had opened the bow doors on arrival in Zeebrugge and was engaged in supervising members of the crew in maintenance and cleaning the ship until he was released from work by the bosun. He then went to his cabin, where he fell asleep and was not awakened by the call 'Harbour Stations', which was given over the tannoy address system. He remained asleep on his bunk until thrown out of it when the *Herald* began to capsize.

The assistant bosun was the most junior 'management' person identified in the incident and this is a clear example of blame being placed at the lowest level in the command chain. It is very evident that the root cause of the disaster was, in fact, a high-level management failure at director level.

The captain or master of the *Herald* on the 6 March 1987 was responsible for the safety of his ship and every person on board and he took the *Herald* to sea with the bow doors fully open. This resulted in tragic consequences and, therefore, he must accept personal responsibility for the loss of his ship. While the full burden of the duty falls to the master to ensure that his ship was, in all respects, ready for sea, subsequent investigations highlight a number of points of mitigation that were made on his behalf, of which there were three principal points.

- First, the master merely followed a system which was operated by all the masters of the *Herald* and approved by the senior master.

- Second, the court was reminded that the orders entitled 'Ship's Standing Orders' issued by the company make no reference, as they should have done, to opening and closing the bow and stern doors.

- Third, before this disaster, there had been no less than five occasions when one of the company's ships had proceeded to sea with bow or stern doors open.

The management, who knew of those incidents, had not brought the matters to the attention of the other masters. The master told the court that if he had been made aware of any of those incidents, he would have instituted a new system under which he would have required that the doors were closed.

> **Help Point:** It was evident that the senior management placed the full weight of responsibility on to the master who was remote from direct influence on members of the board. The master at sea relies on communication regarding incidents that occur on other vessels and should be part of the monitoring feedback process. Senior management failed to communicate important safety information and, when there was a failure, absolved themselves from having any responsibility and passed the blame onto the master of the vessel.

This is clear evidence of a failure in the management system, where senior management knew, or should have known, that there was a hazard with a high severity risk outcome which placed both crew and passengers in a potentially unsafe situation. This was exasperated by the fact that one of the five masters who took it in turn to command the *Herald* was the senior master and one of the functions as senior master was to act as a co-ordinator between all the masters and officers of the ship, in order to achieve uniformity in the practices operated by the different crews.

It can be seen that the errors or omissions on the part of the master, the chief officer, the assistant bosun and the failure of the senior master combined to be the root cause. However, a full investigation into all the circumstances of the disaster determined that serious faults lay higher up in the company in that, for some unknown reason, the board of directors did not appreciate their responsibilities for the safe management of their ships. In fact, all concerned in management, from the members of the board of directors down to junior superintendents, were guilty of fault in that they must be regarded as sharing responsibility for the failure of management. In the Sheen Report there is the now famous statement:

'from top to bottom the body corporate was infected with the disease of sloppiness ... The failure on the part of the shore management to give proper and clear directions was a contributory cause of the disaster ...'.

➢ **Help Point**: Management at director level had knowledge of what was going on aboard the vessel but there was no leadership from the top and the tragic outcome was a result of this.

Based upon the evidence of the case, the Director of Public Prosecutions (DPP) instituted a corporate manslaughter prosecution. It was also considered that while the company was charged with manslaughter, any legal actions should reach every person, whatever their employment status and, therefore, two representatives of senior management, the assistant bosun, the bosun, the chief officer, and the two captains were charged with manslaughter.

➢ **Help point:** It will be noted that the legal actions were unable to address the situation that the failure had its foundation with the board directors. It was they who failed to manage the company and that failure was endemic throughout the corporate structure. With no leadership, a disaster occurred and none of the directors onshore were faced with manslaughter charges.

The failures

2.5 In July 1984, the company had issued a general instruction which defined that it was the duty of the officer loading the main vehicle deck to ensure that the bow doors were *secure when leaving port*. Evidence was forthcoming that the instruction had been regularly disregarded and had been viewed as meaning that it was the task of the loading officer only to see that someone was at the controls and ready to close the doors. That was not the management's intention through the instruction, which was not worded clearly, and, as a consequence, it was not followed. If the instruction had been clear and followed the disaster would not have occurred. The evidence showed that it was the culture of the officers that they always felt under pressure to leave the berth immediately after the completion of loading. This culture spread to the officer on the car deck who would call the bridge and tell the quartermaster to give the order 'harbour stations' over the tannoy, often before loading had been completed.

➢ **Help Point**: Although instructions were issued, they were not suitable for those who had to work to them and there is no evidence that there had been any training as to the need to adopt the procedures. It appears that, while there were instructions, there was no system of review or audit to determine if the procedures were suitable and that staff abided by them. This is a fundamental foundation of the management of safety.

The officer of the watch was the loading officer and that caused a conflict in his duties. This problem was brought to the attention of management by a memorandum, dated 21 August 1982, from the senior master of *Free Enterprise VIII*, in which he said:

> 'Departure from Port:
>
> It is impractical for the Officer of the Watch (either the chief or second officer) to be on the bridge 15 minutes before sailing time. Both are fully committed to loading the ship. At sailing time, the chief officer stands by the bow or stern door to see the ramp out and assure papers are on board etc. The second officer proceeds to his stern mooring station to assure that the propellers are clear and report to the bridge'.

This is further compounded by a damming internal memorandum dated 18 August 1986 sent to assistant managers by the operations manager at Zeebrugge:

> 'There seems to be a general tendency of satisfaction if the ship has sailed two or three minutes early. Where, a full load is present, then every effort has to be made to sail the ship 15 minutes earlier ... I expect to read from now onwards, especially where FE8 is concerned, that the ship left 15 minutes early ... put pressure on the first officer if you don't think he is moving fast enough. Have your load ready when the vessel is in and marshal your staff and machines to work efficiently. Let's put the record straight, sailing late out of Zeebrugge isn't on. It's 15 minutes early for us'.

The evidence that there was pressure on the deck officers was clear to the court even though the company stated that the disaster could have been avoided if the chief officer had stayed on the car deck for another three minutes. The failure was that the company took no formal action to ensure that the chief officer remained on the car deck until the bow doors were closed. The Ship's Standing Orders issued by the company made no reference, as to the operating of the bow and stern doors. The court was told that before the disaster there had been other occasions when one of the company's ships had sailed with bow or stern doors open. A crucial element in this case is that the management knew about some of those incidents, and yet they had not done anything about it.

➢ **Help Point:** Of all the many faults which combined to lead directly or indirectly to this tragic disaster, that of chief officer was the most immediate. The corporation's management system, which was in operation for all vessels, was fundamentally flawed, but it did not remove the personal responsibility of the captain for taking his ship to sea in an unsafe condition. By doing so he was seriously negligent in the carrying out of his duties and that negligence was one of the contributing causes of the accident.

An internal memorandum dated 22 November 1986, addressed to the chief superintendent stated:

'The existing system of deck officer manning for the *Blue Riband Class* ship that relieves on the Zeebrugge run is unsatisfactory. When *Herald* took up the Zeebrugge service our deck officers were reduced from the usual complement of fifteen to ten. The surplus five were distributed round the fleet ... Due to this system, together with trainee master moves, *Herald* will have had a total of exactly 30 different deck officers on the books during the period 29 September to 5 January 1987 ... Many of the transient officers are only here for a few duties and in these circumstances, their main concern is to get the ship loaded and undertake a safe passage between ports. Although they are generally good officers, it is unrealistic to expect them to become involved in the checking of installations and equipment or the detailed organisation of this particular vessel which they do not regard as their own ...'.

In a memorandum dated 28 January 1987 the captain stated:

'I wish to stress again that *Herald* badly needs a *permanent* complement of good deck officers. Our problem was outlined in my memo of 22 November. Since then the throughput of officers has increased even further, partly because of sickness. During the period from 1 September 1986 to 28 January 1987, a total of 36 deck officers have been attached to the ship. We have also lost two masters (Hammond and Irving) and gained one (Robinson). To make matters worse the vessel has had an unprecedented seven changes in sailing schedule. The result has been a serious loss in continuity. Shipboard maintenance, safety gear checks, crew training and the overall smooth running of the vessel have all suffered ...'.

➢ **Help Point:** A wider view into the events that led up to the disaster identifies that the underlying faults lay higher up in the company with the board of directors. It is alleged that they did not appreciate or understand their responsibilities for the safe management of their ships. Therefore, they did not apply their minds to the subject of what directions should have been given to all levels for the safety of their ships. Evidence showed that all concerned in management, from the members of the board of directors down to the junior superintendents, failed in their obligations and duties and must be regarded as being party to the failures of management. If the culture of a company is such that safety is not an intrinsic part of the corporate management then it will be destined for failure.

Information such as the Merchant Shipping Notice No M 1188, July 1986, entitled 'Good Ship Management' was available. The advice given in that Notice included the following points:

'The efficient and safe operation of ships requires the exercise of good management both at sea and ashore ... The overall responsibility of the shipping company requires the need for close involvement by management ashore. To this end it is recommended that every company operating ships should designate a person ashore with responsibility for monitoring the technical and safety aspects of the operation of its ships and for providing appropriate shore based back-up ... Stress is placed upon the importance of providing the master with clear instructions to him and his officers. The instructions should include adequate Standing Orders. There should be close co-operation and regular and effective communication in both directions between ship and shore'.

➤ **Help Point**: The above advice is very sound and it could be argued that in a well-managed ship-owning company, such advice should not have been necessary to ensure that its operational procedures complied with the information provided. While the Sheen Report only identifies one example of how the standard of management fell short of the recommendations contained in that Notice, it reveals a culture of complacency.

'On the 18 March 1986 there was a meeting of senior masters with management, at which Mr Devlin was in the chair. One of the topics raised for discussion concerned the recognition of the chief officer as head of the Department and the roles of the maintenance master and chief officer. Mr Devlin said, although he was still considering writing definitions of these different roles, he felt *it was more preferable not to define the roles but to allow them to evolve* ... Clear instructions are the foundation of a safe system of operation. It was the failure to give clear orders about the duties of the officers on the Zeebrugge run, which contributed so greatly to the causes of the disaster ... it was not the responsibility of Mr Devlin to see that the Company orders were properly drafted...*who was responsible?*..."Well in truth, nobody, though there ought to have been." The board of directors must accept a heavy responsibility for their lamentable lack of directions. Individually and collectively they lacked a sense of responsibility.'

Note: Mr Devlin was the Chief Marine Superintendent and in 1986 he became a Director of the company.

Other failures on the part of the management included their role in the poor culture that infected the company and this is a matter for public concern. The culture was, in part, formed through the failures in the Standing Orders, which made no reference to closing the bow and stern doors, and they appear to have led the captain to assume that his ship was ready for sea in all respects, merely because he had no report to the contrary. Most importantly was the failure to identify or accept responsibility at director level. This was identified in that Mr Devlin was prepared to accept that he was responsible for the safe operation of the company's ships and added that he thought that before he joined the board, the safety of the ships was a collective board responsibility. Mr Ayers, another director, told the court that no director was solely responsible for safety.

> **Help Point**: In a company where there is no positive health and safety culture, the board members will *not* identify and accept responsibility to adopt a change of culture. Ownership through leadership will provide the positive momentum.

In examining the culture of the management, flaws were identified when Mr Devlin was asked who was responsible for considering matters relating to safety in the navigation of the company's ships. His answer was that it was ashore where the system would be to take a consensus of the senior master's views. However, as the investigation developed, it became clear that the management onshore took virtually no notice of what they were told by their ships masters. This was highlighted when it was stated that there was one period of two and a half years during which there was no formal meeting between management and the senior masters. The Marine Department did not listen to the complaints, suggestions or wishes of their masters.

> **Help Point**: There was a culture within the company that the shore staff of the company were well aware of the possibility that one of their ships could sail with the stern or bow doors open and took no action. Furthermore, they were aware of the very sensible and basic device in the form of indicator lights that would indicate the status of the doors on the bridge, which had been suggested by responsible masters but ignored by management. Those charged with the management of the company's Ro-Ro fleet were not qualified to deal with many nautical matters and were unwilling to listen to their masters, who were well qualified, and so did not provide the confidence and backing of the management.

The outcome of the trial of *R v P&O European Ferries (Dover) Ltd* was terminated when the judge gave directions to the jury that, because of the law, there was no evidence available upon which they could convict six of the eight defendants, including the company, of manslaughter.

In terms of general safety and risk management, the test balanced against the facts of the case are a cause for concern. It could be argued that even to a person with no marine experience, a ferry leaving port with its bow doors open, exposing a large, open car deck is an obvious risk to the vessel. Management engaged in the ferry business who evaluated the risks posed to their ships, need only look back into history to identify the incident of the Irish Sea car ferry, *Princess Victoria*, which sank on 31 January 1953 with a loss of 128 lives. At the inquest, a member of the crew stated that the ferry had sailed with the cargo doors open. A wave hit the ship and water swept onto the car deck moving the cargo to the starboard side of the vessel causing it to list. Another dramatic incident occurred much closer in time and should have alerted ferry operators to risks and potential outcomes when the roll-on, roll-off ferry, *European Gateway*, capsized off Harwich in 1982. Six people were killed in the incident. In 1985, the Royal Institute of Naval Architects identified the need to change the design of the roll-on, roll-off vessels before there was a major incident with a large loss of life. None of the warnings were heeded and it was only two years later that the pre-determined disaster occurred when the *Herald of Free Enterprise* capsized.

> **Help Point**: The importance of management responding to previous incidents and near misses is an essential component of effective safety management. In this case, it was a classic failure of board level management not being leaders.

The Southall Railway disaster

2.6   The dramatic newspaper headlines of an article in the *Daily Express*, 3 July 1999, by J Twomey declared, 'Judge attacks Government for failure to bring in law of corporate killing – No one can be tried over this carnage'. It was the opening of an article reporting on the corporate manslaughter trial of Great Western Trains. The judge launched a stinging attack on the Government as he threw out manslaughter charges against a railway company which had been accused of the deaths of seven passengers.

The case of Great Western Trains (GWT) (*R v Great Western Trains Co Ltd [2000] QB 796*) involved the 10.32 am Swansea to London Paddington train, which was driven by Larry Harrison. The train, which was an Inter City 125, passed through a red signal at 125 mph and crashed into a freight train near Southall Station in West London. The train was fitted with two safety devices, which could have prevented the incident, but neither was working. As a result, the company was charged with corporate manslaughter and the train driver with individual manslaughter. It was anticipated that the managing director of GWT, Richard George, would be personally charged with manslaughter because of his responsibility to ensure trains follow adequate safety procedures. The train driver had looked down to pack his bag and therefore not seen the red signal. The case against him was dropped because it was said that the crash had left him psychologically unfit to face trial. That case for the Crown failed because it failed to identify a senior figure within GWT who was the *directing mind and will* and who failed to ensure the safety of the passengers.

➢ **Help Point:** Corporate manslaughter continues to be an issue where unless an individual can be identified as being a controlling mind with direct involvement with the incident, then there is no case. Individuals, often employees, face manslaughter charges for having carried out an act which was a consequence of management failure. The public and pressure groups do not like this situation and press for a change in the law.

The case named above was a landmark case and focused on the prosecution of a large corporation, ie Great Western Trains Ltd, for corporate manslaughter, which was terminated by the Old Bailey judge, Mr Justice Scott Baker. The impact of this ruling for the future of corporate manslaughter prosecutions means that no large organisation can ever be prosecuted for manslaughter unless there is a radical change in the law. The judge rebuked ministers for failing to act on the recommendations of the Law Commission three years earlier to introduce a new offence of corporate killing.

The *Daily Express* article continued to state that:

'Attorney General, John Morris, is to appeal against the findings ... The case against the company foundered on an age old principle ... For the prosecution to succeed, the Crown had to identify a senior figure within GWT who was the *directing mind and will,* and who failed to ensure the safety of the passengers'.

This again defines the basis of corporate manslaughter failings, which was clarified by the judge who said:

'The only basis on which the prosecution may, in law, advance a case against Great Western Trains for manslaughter is by identifying some person within the company whose gross negligence was that of Great Western Trains itself. The only candidate would be managing director, Richard George, who was responsible for all matters of safety. In the absence of Mr George having procured, authorised or directed any tortuous act, he cannot be guilty of manslaughter. Consequently, neither can Great Western Trains ... were the law otherwise; a conviction would mark public abhorrence of a slipshod safety system leading to seven deaths and may injured victims'.

In addition to the charge of corporate manslaughter against Great Western Trains being dropped, the train driver, Larry Harrison, walked free after the prosecution stated that the crash had left him psychologically unfit to face trial and so he took early retirement and will receive a pension. In reviewing the case, it was accepted that the train was faulty because the automatic warning and protection systems were not working and there was no second driver in the cab. However, he was the driver and was under a duty to undertake his work task correctly and he failed to do so. The trial would have lasted several weeks and Mr Harrison would have been unable to pay a fine and would probably been unfit to serve a prison sentence.

➤ **Help Point**: Again there is a situation where an individual is left to face the legal consequences. He was an employee who followed procedures, but on the day in question, was directed by management to take a train on a journey with a safety device not functioning. So here was an individual under pressure from management to carry out a work task with known potential risks and, because of the corporate culture, he broke the rules. Had he taken the train on the journey on his own volition then the gross negligence could have been his alone, but he was the victim of a corporate culture of management failure.

Ladbroke Grove railway disaster

2.7   On 5 October 1999, a train passed a red signal at Ladbroke Grove and continued on for some 700 metres into the path of a high-speed train. As a result of the collision and the subsequent fires, 31 people died and 227 were taken to hospital.

An inquiry followed the incident and in the Ladbroke Grove Rail Inquiry Part 2, Executive Summary by Lord Cullen, it is identified that there were several incidents where drivers had crossed this signal (SN 109) at red and it was reported at the inquiry that following the seventh and eight time the signal was passed at danger (SPAD), Mr David Franks, the Production Director of Thames Trains, informed the inquiry that as both SPADs had involved experienced drivers and in view of the failure to carry out remedial action, he stated:

'I insisted that Railtrack should accept that the primary cause of these SPADs was the signalling equipment itself. I accepted the drivers had some responsibility but this was not the root cause'.

In his report, Lord Cullen stated in the summary at 1.15:

'The evidence clearly demonstrated that the rail industry needs to develop the ability to behave as a learning organisation. I identify a number of areas of importance. Firstly, identifying unsafe acts and conditions and taking prompt steps to deal with them. Secondly, applying and disseminating the lessons of accidents and incidents (including near misses). Here the evidence showed the process was inhibited by the "blame culture", and the lack of a co-ordinated system for the collation of recommendations and ensuring that they were followed up. Thirdly, using risk assessment in order to drive improvements in safety. Fourthly, gaining benefit from the process of auditing. This has been less than fully effective. Fifthly, using data and analytical tools. The evidence shows there were weaknesses in the industry's use of these materials. Sixthly, training with particular reference to refresher courses, into which greater effort requires to be put'.

Further, at 1.16, Lord Cullen states:

'Finally I direct attention to the desirability of the industry developing a culture in which there is a progressive movement from a situation where management make the rules and tell employees what to do, to a situation where individuals can contribute ideas and effort, while complying with the rules and procedures, through to a position where there is a committed, dedicated team approach, with a high degree of interdependency between teams and across company boundaries'.

➢ **Help Point**: All of the disasters referred too above had warning signs that were either ignored or not given full management attention. There are now effective databases available to log and track close out of actions regarding all safety incidents and near misses. Remote work sites are able to input their incident details directly into a database so there is an immediate degree of ownership, and the systems have the capability to alert all work sites to any accident or high potential near miss. For a large company, software can also group incidents and near misses to assist senior management to analyse trends with high potential near misses.

To conform with Lord Cullen's recommendations to enable employees to contribute ideas and effort, local management teams can be formed to close out their own incidents and implement improvements and, on a regular basis, senior management can review the incidents and confirm their approval of the improvement measures taken by the local teams. A team from senior management with operational and engineering skills can be established to monitor trends and, having recognised a trend, may request line management to issue a series of measures to mitigate against further incidents.

The Hatfield Railway disaster

2.8   The Hatfield rail crash happened at 12.23 pm on 17 October 2000 when the high-speed Great North Eastern Railway (GNER) train left King's Cross Station, bound for Leeds. The train was travelling at 115 mph when it was derailed by a broken rail between Welham Green and Hatfield Stations. Four people were killed and 104 were injured in the accident, which revealed network-wide problems with cracked tracks. Railtrack swiftly admitted that a broken rail caused the accident and it later emerged that both it and Balfour Beatty, who were responsible for maintaining that stretch of track, had known ten months before the accident that the rail was in need of replacement. Six managers were charged with manslaughter on

14 July 2003 in connection with the crash. The manslaughter charge carries a maximum penalty of life imprisonment.

Media reports stated that British Transport Police had charged six men and the two companies with manslaughter due to gross negligence and an offence under the Health and Safety at Work etc Act 1974 (HSWA 1974). Those charged with manslaughter were:

- the director of the London North East Zone of Railtrack;

- the area asset manager of the London North East Zone (South) of Railtrack;

- the regional director until 11 August 2000 of Balfour Beatty;

- a civil engineer for Balfour Beatty; and

- a track engineer of the London North Eastern Zone of Railtrack.

Media reports stated that Gerald Corbett, the former chief executive of Railtrack, now Network Rail, and Chris Leah, the director of safety at Network Rail are among six others who are charged with offences under the HSWA 1974. In November 2000, Gerald Corbett, the former Railtrack chief executive, admitted after the incident that the track was in an appalling and totally unacceptable condition and that there should have been a speed restriction. He further stated that there were a multitude of other things that should have happened but did not. He had told the Commons Transport Select Committee that Railtrack and Balfour Beatty had failed.

Network Rail, the Government-backed company which took over Railtrack's responsibilities for maintaining track and stations last year, is to be liable for any offences committed by its predecessor. The company will defend itself and its employees against the charges. Balfour Beatty, the engineering company that maintained the stretch of track where the accident happened, plans to defend itself against the charges. The crash prompted Railtrack, which was then responsible for 23,000 miles of line, to impose hundreds of speed limits, causing widespread disruption from which the industry has yet to recover. Railtrack was put into administration as a result of the losses brought about by this incident having previously been a profitable entity.

Potters Bar railway disaster

2.9   In an article by Dipesh Gadher in *The Sunday Times*, 24 August 2003, the headlines stated: 'Rail Contractor to Escape Potters Bar Death Charges'.

The Potters Bar railway crash happened in May 2002 after the last coach of a four-carriage train travelling from London to Cambridge derailed when passing over points at Potters Bar station in Hertfordshire. An HSE report earlier in 2003 stated that nuts were absent from the rear stretcher bar of the points and that the appropriate lock mechanism was worn out. This ruled out the likelihood of sabotage, which was a claim made by Jarvis, the maintenance company, immediately after the derailment. The HSE report concluded that the poor condition of the points 'resulted from inappropriate adjustment and from insufficient maintenance'.

The Sunday Times article revealed that executives at Jarvis, the company at the centre of the investigation into the rail crash, were expected to escape manslaughter charges. The reason given is that the police believed there was insufficient evidence for a criminal case against the engineering contractor despite an investigation lasting 15 months.

The final decision rested with the Crown Prosecution Service (CPS) where lawyers would have reviewed the evidence gathered and compiled by British Transport Police (BTP) investigators. This is said to have consisted of more than 1,300 statements as well as CCTV footage from station cameras which was sent to the FBI in America for analysis.

Jarvis, however, still faced the possibility of being brought to court for alleged breaches of health and safety laws. This meant that if the CPS decided not to proceed with manslaughter charges then the case could be taken up by the HSE which had been carrying out a parallel investigation. The families of those killed and injured wanted to pursue a damages claim against Jarvis and Railtrack, the company which managed Britain's rail infrastructure at the time of the tragedy. But they had been denied legal aid and were, at that time, unable to fund a case in the civil courts which could have forced the two firms to admit liability for the crash. The key argument was that even if the CPS was unable to bring manslaughter charges it did not mean that a case cannot be proven in a civil court that, on the balance of probabilities, Railtrack and Jarvis were to blame.

The article raised the issue where Jarvis executives had provoked outrage when they raised the prospect of escaping serious criminal charges. Noel Broadbent, the company's director of compliance and standards, predicted the police would 'give up' soon. Paris Moayedi, Jarvis' chairman, also drew criticism by claiming that the HSE's findings had 'no concrete backing'. In the emotive confrontation by the two sides, Perdita Kark, whose father, Austen, former head of the BBC World Service, was killed and whose mother, the author Nina Bawden, was badly injured quoted as saying: 'This is absolute rubbish and it is deeply offensive'.

In a book about leadership management it should be considered that, whilst any undertaking will want to defend itself against serious legal charges, adverse statements from the senior management will only inflame the public perception of a 'don't care' corporate culture. It is another factor where when faced with disaster, a leader will face up to the responsibilities and manage the situation. Trial by the courts is preferable to trial by media for everybody concerned.

The Concorde disaster

2.10   Not all disasters occur in the UK and it is of value to briefly examine some that have wider implications. One disaster which received dramatic real time media coverage involved Concorde. Drawing reference from the facts from Bureau Enquetes-Accident report into the incident on 25 July 2000 at La Patte D'Oie in Gonesse (95) to the Concorde registered F-BTSC, operated by Air France. Interim report 15/12/2000 which provides the following information:

> 'On 25 July 2000 an Air France Concorde crashed killing 113 people. The plane was bound for New York but crashed into a hotel at Gonesse on the outskirts of Paris after taking off from Roissy Charles de Gaulle airport. The interim Bureau Enquetes-Accidents report states the aircraft took off with a large stabilised flame coming from the wing that caused structural damage throughout the flight. It is suggested that a tyre had burst on take off and debris had punctured a fuel tank and the escaping kerosene had caught fire'.

The more technical explanation states:

> 'The aircraft was flying low and at slow speed and control of the aircraft was lost as a result of thrust asymmetry due to profound thrust drag imbalance and, perhaps, to structural damage caused by the fire'.

It is important to recall there had been previous incidents where wing fuel tanks had been punctured due to debris flying up and, of specific note, was an incident to another Concorde aircraft in June 1979. In this case, a Concorde taking off from Washington Dulles airport suffered a burst tyre and the destruction of a wheel which caused perforations to the wing tanks. After some unsuccessful attempts to retract the landing gear after take off, the crew landed the aircraft back at Washington after 24 minutes. A detailed investigation into the near miss was made and several engineering and operational improvements were made, including a system for detecting main landing gear tyre under inflation, improved protection in the normal breaking hydraulic system, installation of new reinforced wheels and new reinforced tyres. It was, however, concluded that it was not necessary to install protection to the underside of the wings.

It is very positive that so much was done to improve Concorde's safety as a result of a near miss but, regrettably, these improvements were not comprehensive enough to prevent the disaster that occurred due to a similar incident. As a result of the Paris disaster, Concorde aircraft were taken out of service for extensive modifications to the wing fuel tanks. They were then given a clean bill of health and took to the air again but Concorde has since been taken out of service completely. Perhaps people were not happy to fly Concorde after the accident?

The Challenger disaster

2.11   The Presidential Commission on the Space Shuttle Challenger Accident Report dated 6 June 1986, reported on the investigation of the Space Shuttle Challenger disaster which, on 28 January 1986, disintegrated seconds after the launch killing all seven people onboard. The Commission concluded the accident was due to the failure in the pressure seal in the aft field joint of the right solid rocket booster. A contributing cause of the accident was determined to be the flawed decision to launch. The Commission concluded that there was a serious management failing in the decision-making process leading up to the flight. A well-structured and managed system emphasising safety would have flagged the rising doubts about the solid rocket booster joint seal and aborted the mission.

The Columbia shuttle disaster

2.12   'The shaming of NASA: How safety was sacrificed and seven astronauts died', was the stark headline in *The Independent*, 27 August, 2003, where David Usborne was reporting on the final report into the *Columbia* shuttle disaster. The National Aeronautics and Space Administration (NASA) stood accused of complacency and negligence after independent investigators attacked the organisation's flawed safety procedures. They found that those procedures were as much to blame for the calamity, in which seven astronauts died, as technical faults. The 248-page report, the product of a $20m (£12.7m) investigation, places the blame on NASA for failing to learn the lessons of the *Challenger* disaster 16 years earlier in which seven astronauts also died.

They also highlighted NASA's failure to heed warnings that insulation foam had broken away, damaging one of the shuttle's wings shortly after take-off. The key issues identified by Usborne include:

- flawed practices at NASA were 'as much a cause' of tragedy as technical faults;

- NASA managers missed at least eight opportunities to evaluate damage to the shuttle;

- pressure to reduce operating costs meant safety upgrades were delayed;

- the mission suffered from 'ineffective leadership' that 'failed to ensure the safety of the crew';

- the report says: 'If these systemic flaws are not resolved, the scene is set for another accident';

- the report highlighted key issues of failure by management and included a 'self-protective culture' at the heart of an organisation that sends human beings on the most high-risk journeys known. That culture meant that NASA's managers accepted increasing levels of risk to the point where they accepted some flaws as being normal in the shuttle system. The investigators found NASA's organisational culture and structure had as much to do with the accident as the external tank foam'.

The investigators identified NASA's top management as showing a 'lack of concern' about the technical problems raised by engineers. The report identified that there was a consistent lack of concern about the debris strike on *Columbia*. An indictment of the management failure was when NASA managers told the investigation that 'there was no safety-of-flight issue' and 'we couldn't have done anything about it anyway'.

The report continues to show that the investigators found that management had failed to act on specific and repeated warnings about the possibility of a disaster for *Columbia* after foam from its fuel tanks struck a wing after its lift-off. The mechanical cause of the disaster was identified long ago: a piece of foam on an external tank, the size of a suitcase, broke of 81 seconds after lift off and punched a hole in the heat-shielding leading edge of the left wing. Upon re-entry, the gash allowed superheated gases to invade the craft's structure and start to melt it.

The investigators identified critical safety failings because there was:

(a) 'ineffective leadership'; and

(b) 'failure to fulfil the implicit contract to do whatever was possible to ensure the safety of the crew'.

A most damning indictment against the management was when engineers at the agency repeatedly raised questions about the possible implications of the debris strike once the shuttle was in orbit. They had approached management on three occasions during the 16-day mission, to ask for satellite photographs of the craft to allow them to check for possible damage to its skin. Those pictures were never made available and a final video inside the crew compartment shows that three crew members had failed to don their prescribed pressure suits, helmets and gloves for re-entry.

The report provides for a substantial number of recommendations for reform, including a shake-up of NASA's managerial structure. However, some blame has been placed on the politicians because NASA has been under consistent pressure to maintain the schedule to keep up with the construction plans for the International Space Station whilst cutting costs at the same time. Congress and NASA leadership exerted constant pressure on all levels of management and the workforce to reduce or at least freeze operating costs with the result that safety and support upgrades were delayed or deferred, with the result that the shuttle infrastructure deteriorated.

Management failures are not reserved for the UK, however, there is a predominance and ongoing catalogue of failures that befalls the UK and it appears that the only option to reverse the trend is to adopt true leadership management.

Failures of management

2.13   The evidence is very clear that the major contributor to the list of disasters lies with management and, more specifically, with senior management. They either appear not to know what is going on within their undertakings or if they do, then that are not acting upon the safety critical information that they receive. The most challenging role in achieving excellence in safety performance is to predict future undesirable events and mitigate against them before they occur. Achieving success in this objective often results in non-events, which means the expected disaster does not occur and it takes self-discipline and effort to maintain the focus. It is relatively easy to measure lagging indicators of safety performance and to respond to actual accidents with improvements, but it is proven that proactive preventative action will improve safety performance. The requirement for near miss or high-potential incident reporting is essential in a business where there is a desire for a positive safety culture. However, there are, unfortunately, many examples where work-related fatalities have occurred which could have been prevented had the warning signals been heeded and management showed leadership.

Chapter 3

The Cost of Corporate Failure

Introduction

3.0   The message that must be understood by management is that following an accident or incident there is a cost. That cost can be in human life, human injury and suffering and the loss of plant or equipment: all impact on the lives and finances of those involved. A director or member of staff facing prosecution inevitably lives out his or her life 'under a cloud' and it may take several years before the case appears in court. It will be evident that there are demands from the public to 'lock directors or managers up' following serious accidents or incidents and this chapter reviews the penalty aspects of getting it wrong.

Getting it right is a valuable lesson and it cannot be emphasised enough that the 'costs' are in the hands of those who manage the undertaking.

The legal cost

3.1   The Health and Safety at Work etc Act 1974 ('the Act') applies to all employees apart from domestic servants in private households. There are problems with the Act, which is basically a criminal statute with determined penalties for breaches. It does not allow for compensation claims.

Until recently, the majority of cases brought under the Act have been dealt with in the Magistrates' Court with the results that there have been limited authoritative interpretations and few legal decisions from the higher courts. The financial penalties arising from the lower courts are restricted to a maximum of £20,000 for certain sections of the Act whilst the Regulations within the Act are subject to a maximum fine of £5,000. However, cases that are referred to the Crown Court are subject to unlimited fines.

The principal objective of the Act has been to make management aware of its obligations towards health and safety in the workplace. Since the introduction of the Act in 1974 there have been numerous health and safety regulations introduced and supported by Approved Codes of Practice (ACoPs). Much of this legislation has been introduced as a result of the UK's membership of the European Union.

➢ **Help point:** An ACoP provides guidance to support a specific regulation and is drafted by the Health & Safety Executive (HSE) and the industry. The latter have ownership of the contents. An ACoP is not law but can be used by the courts to determine a standard by which an undertaking must aspire.

Enforcement action taken against directors or employees is based upon breaches of the Act or supporting Regulations. While it is generally expected that the businesses identified as 'undertakings' so as to encompass those that are incorporated as well as those that are not, such as partnerships and trusts, will generally face prosecution, there are specific offences available to be laid against individuals. It has generally been understood that it is difficult to gather sufficient evidence to prosecute individuals, particularly directors, under section 37 of the HSWA 1974. However, the emphasis by the enforcing authorities has changed and individuals are to be held accountable, and so it is anticipated that more prosecutions of individuals can be expected.

It could be argued that if the current status of fines and use of imprisonment were effective, the level of workplace incidents would have reduced but they still remain at an unacceptable high level. An answer could be that there needs to be a review and radical change in the legal process and punishment options available to the courts.

The introduction of the Government's Revitalising Health and Safety Programme in 2000 was seen as a way ahead, but there appears to be a reluctance on behalf of the Government to introduce a punishment and sanctions package of fines and imprisonment as options of ensuring compliance with health and safety legislation.

A major factor that limits the effectiveness of enforcement and punishment, which is explored in this chapter, is that there is no legal stipulation that requires an organisation, even though public companies have audited accounts published, to disclose its financial status through an accredited source, such as a firm of accountants. There is only an obligation for an undertaking to provide general figures and the same rules apply to directors, managers and self-employed persons.

Often defendants declare poverty and state that heavy fines will mean redundancies among staff or that a financial penalty will take money from public services and courts are loath to punish those who are not implicated in the offence, which can be employees or the general public. These situations may well be true but, if there is no formal evidence obtained to substantiate the financial situation, the family or other interested parties may consider there to be a failure of the justice system.

Industry leaders' views

3.2   An article in the *Health and Safety Bulletin* 307, April 2002, states:

'Most industry leaders rank safety low on their list of business priorities, according to a British Safety Council (BSC)-MORI survey. The findings will disappoint the HSC, which has tried in recent years both to make a business case for safety and to make safety a boardroom issue. The attitudes also fly in the face of increasing Government pressure to reduce workplace injuries and ill health.

Nearly 100 board directors (mainly chairs, presidents and managing directors) of FTSE 500 companies responded to the survey carried out in November 2001.When asked to list their three main corporate objectives, only one in six (16%) singled out improving safety in the working environment, although this represents a 3% increase on the 2000 survey. One in two manufacturing directors lists safety in their top three priorities. Across industry, generating profits for shareholders (84%) and increasing customer satisfaction (80%) continue to be the top objectives, with the desire for new products and services, maximising productivity and better training for staff all placed ahead of improving safety'.

The article gives the impression that the author is criticising senior managers for putting profit first. In many cases it is quite right that profit is first providing that profit and safety do not clash, and we are at a disadvantage because we do not know how the survey was worded which will influence the results.

The balance must be to have the safety priority included in the profit priority and be aware of complacency which may lead senior managers to think that they have done enough. There is, however, the need for senior management to keep safety on the agenda to limit their exposure to culpability:

'Most of the directors interviewed are making preparations for the Government's proposed corporate killing legislation and only one in eight say they would be likely to, or would resign their directorships because of the new offences. The most popular preparations are demonstrating a commitment to health and safety (51%), setting up effective health and safety Communications (41%), and appointing a health and safety director (35%).

Four in five directors (86%) think loss of their company's reputation would be a long-term effect of a successful prosecution for corporate killing, and about half think it would create employee morale problems and raise insurance costs. Seven in ten believe such legal action would have some effect on their companies' share prices and nearly two-thirds believe that their institutional investors would demand corrective action'.

Whatever the arguments and counter arguments, the authors consider that there is a case for custodial sentences for the most serious workplace accidents, in particular, where there has been neglect on behalf of the most senior officials. It should be pointed out that employees are not exempt from receiving a custodial sentence if they act negligently by disobeying procedures or using the wrong tool. The question that must be addressed is to the degree of culpability of the defendant on each occasion and that is a matter for the courts.

Enforcement against companies and their officers

3.3   A business, no matter its type of formation, be it a company limited in its liability, a partnership, trust or a self-employed individual, they can all face enforcement sanctions from the authorities such as the HSE and local authority inspectors. Enforcement can be in the form of an official letter, an Improvement or Prohibition Notice or prosecution in either the Magistrates' or Crown Courts. The letter can be deemed an official warning but the notices are legally binding and must be complied with. Enforcement must not be confused with punishment, which can only be administered by the courts.

It is a fundamental principle of company law that, from the date of incorporation, a company is an artificial legal person with rights and duties distinct from its members or directors. However, the limited liability provided by incorporation does not at present protect individuals from criminal liability nor will the proposed new offence of corporate killing of itself increase or decrease individual liability.

Therefore, action against individual directors or officers might be justified, even in cases where an undertaking found guilty of corporate killing could pay the fine imposed by the court and/or comply with a remedial order. This means that any individual who could be shown to have had some influence on, or responsibility for, the circumstances in which a management failure falling far below what could reasonably be expected, was a cause of a person's death, should be subject to disqualification, from acting in a management role in any undertaking, carrying on a business or activity in Great Britain.

The ground for disqualification would not be that of causing the death but of contributing to the management failure resulting in death. It is envisaged that a separate proceeding would usually be brought against individual officer(s) following the conviction of the company on indictment. The disqualification of culpable company directors from a role in managing any undertaking would make evasion of a disqualification order much more difficult. It is intended that a person disqualified from acting as a director under such circumstances should not be able to join a partnership as a way of circumventing the disqualification order.

The aim is to make 'undertakings' more accountable in law where a person dies because of a failure on the part of the directors. If there was sufficient evidence, an individual officer could be charged with one of the new manslaughter offences, ie killing by gross carelessness or reckless killing, whether or not proceedings were brought against the undertaking for the new corporate killing offence.

It would not be possible for an individual officer automatically to be made criminally liable on the sole basis of the conviction of an undertaking for the corporate offence. It would be necessary for him to be charged with an offence which he has committed and be given the chance to defend himself against it. In order to go down this route, it would be necessary to create an additional criminal offence in respect of substantially contributing to the corporate offence of the undertaking in question leading to the death of a person.

A report on health and safety offences and penalties for 2000/01 the police referred 43 cases of work-related death to the Crown Prosecution Service (CPS), in sectors where the HSE are the enforcing authority to consider possible manslaughter charges. The CPS have started five manslaughter prosecutions. Since 1992, a total of 224 manslaughter cases have been referred to the CPS. They have brought 55 manslaughter prosecutions, 11 of which have resulted in convictions.

Corporate manslaughter

3.4   At the time of writing, there are four successful corporate manslaughter prosecutions as well as a number of unsuccessful cases. The most notable failure and a driving force for changes in the law was the sinking of the *Herald of Free Enterprise* and the prosecution of P&O European Ferries (Dover) Ltd for corporate manslaughter.

The four successful cases have one factor in common in that they are small organisations where the management has a more 'hands on' involvement than in a larger corporation.

OLL Limited

3.5   In December 1994, OLL Limited (formerly Active Leisure and Learning Ltd) became the first company in English legal history to be convicted of the common law crime of manslaughter. The company was fined £60,000. Peter Kite, the managing director, aged 45, also became the first director to be given an immediate custodial sentence for a manslaughter conviction arising from the operation of a business and was sentenced to three years' imprisonment (reduced to two years on appeal). Both defendants were found guilty on four counts of manslaughter arising from the deaths of four teenagers on 22 March 1993.

Jackson Transport (Ossett) Limited

3.6   In 1996, Jackson Transport (Ossett) Limited was convicted of Corporate Manslaughter and fined £22,000. Its director, Alan Jackson, was convicted of the manslaughter of one of his employees and jailed for twelve months and fined £1,500.00.

The case centered on twenty-one year old James Hodgson, an employee of the company who died less than an hour after being splashed with a deadly chemical while cleaning the inside of a chemical tanker at Jackson Transport's base in West Ossett, Yorkshire. Mr Hodgson was carrying out a dangerous cleaning job protected only by a pair of overalls and a baseball cap. Special suits for protection against chemical risks were only provided to the tanker drivers of the vehicles, and those available were in poor condition and there were no hats, visors or goggles.

English Brothers Limited

3.7   'Construction company guilty of corporate manslaughter' was the headline of the HSE Press Notice dated 3 August 2001. English Brothers Ltd, a construction company, was convicted as a result of a prosecution brought by the CPS.

The fatality involved Bill Larkman who was employed as a gang foreman for the erection of an onion store on a farm at The Crofts, Newton, near Wisbech in Cambridgeshire. Mr Larkman was working on the roof in June 1999 when the accident occurred. Although there were no witnesses to the event, it is thought that he lost his footing when roofing material slipped causing him to fall more than eight metres to his death. The seriousness of the incident was enhanced because HSE inspectors had found Larkman on another site without the correct safety equipment being used. The matter was taken up with the company who agreed to remedy the problem but they failed to take any action.

This failure meant that the incident occurred not as an oversight but as a failure of management to take action. That failure amounted to gross negligence. Melvyn Hubbard, a director, was also charged with manslaughter but after the company pleaded guilty to manslaughter, those charges were not proceeded with. The company was fined £25,000 for manslaughter. In addition there was a fine of £5,000 for an offence under section 3 of the Health and Safety at Work etc Act 1974 for failing to ensure the health and safety of people not in its employment. The company was also ordered to pay prosecution costs of £12,500. The financial penalty against the company was said to have amounted to one year's profit for the organisation.

Teglagaard Hardwood Limited

3.8 The outcome of a trial in 2003, discussed in the *Safety and Health Practitioner*, April 2003, involved the UK subsidiary of a Danish company, Teglagaard Hardwood, which was found guilty of corporate manslaughter.

In April 2000, Christopher Longrigg had been working at the firm's dockside timber yard. He was standing next to one of several five-metre high stacks of hardwood timber in the yard, when they began to collapse towards him. As he tried to run away, the stack fell over and trapped him underneath and he was instantly crushed to death. Witnesses gave evidence saying that they saw stacks of timber swaying in the breeze. The company had no safety policy, no risk assessments and no safe stacking procedures. None of the staff had received any training.

Guilty pleas to manslaughter charges were entered by both the company and a director, John Horner Snr. In sentencing, the judge stated:

'your arrogance and callous indifference led to the death of Christopher. It was a tragic accident, a result, at best indifference, at worst of an arrogant approach to health and safety'.

John Horner Snr was found guilty of manslaughter and was given a fifteen month prison sentence, suspended for two years. The Company was fined £25,000.

Corporate killing

3.9 In March 1996, the Law Commission published a report entitled 'Legislating the Criminal Code – Involuntary Manslaughter' (No 237, HMSO, 1996). The draft Bill which accompanied the report set out the elements of the proposed offence.

The Law Commission proposals were similar to the duties to ensure safety imposed by the HSWA 1974. However, the shortcomings of managers and employees must be grossly negligent rather than simply negligent. This would facilitate imposing a penalty, which is more closely related to the degree of wrongdoing. At present, the penalties for health and safety offences are unlimited in the Crown Court and the practical difference from any change in the law of corporate manslaughter would be a higher penalty and a higher degree of opprobrium.

A Home Office working group considered the law of manslaughter generally and the question of corporate manslaughter, and issued the consultative document, 'Reforming the Law on Involuntary Manslaughter: The Government's Proposals', May 2000 (Home Office Communication Directorate).

Among the key issues that arise from the proposals are that the offence of corporate killing could apply to undertakings as used in the HSWA 1974. Although an undertaking is not specifically defined in the Act, the HSE have relied on the definition provided in the Local Employment Act 1960 where it is described as 'any trade or business or other activity providing employment'.

Clearly, the use of the word 'undertaking' would greatly broaden the scope of the offence. It would encompass a range of organisations which have not been classified as corporations to include schools, hospital trusts, partnerships and unincorporated charities, as well as small businesses, such as self-employed gas fitters.

In effect, the offence of corporate killing would apply to all employing organisations including subcontractors. It is estimated that this would mean a total of 3.5 million enterprises might become potentially liable to the offence of corporate killing.

If an undertaking is found guilty of corporate killing, directors of that undertaking could face disqualification from holding any office that involved the management or control of any enterprise. In addition, the Law Commission recommends that the court should have the power to make remedial orders, either where HSE (or other appropriate enforcement body) has not issued a notice or where such a notice had not been complied with. No new enforcement powers would be necessary to allow this approach (see HSWA 1974, s 42).

Any change in the law would mean that a company would have to address safety issues at board level or risk conviction for corporate manslaughter. There would certainly be far more investigations following deaths at work. This would be to identify if there was gross negligence which would require investigations to continue beyond the point where there was sufficient evidence to conclude that a company was simply negligent. The net effect of more investigation, more prosecutions for corporate killing and a greater likelihood of conviction should be to increase safety awareness, particularly in areas where low standards currently prevail.

The Government's original proposals were that the new legislation would include undertakings as well as individuals, however, at the time of writing, the information from the Home Office is that any new law would only involve organisations and that there would not be any new offences for individuals. The proposals appear to focus on the issues summarised below.

Involuntary Homicide Act 1995, s 4(1)

3.10 This section identifies the basis of the corporate offence which determines that a corporation is guilty of corporate killing if:

(a) management failure by the corporation is the cause or one of the causes of a person's death; and

(b) that failure constitutes conducts falling far below what can reasonably be expected of the corporation in the circumstances.

The key issue in (a) above is that of management failure. The onus will be on the prosecution to prove, *beyond all reasonable doubt* (the test in criminal law), that there was a management failure and that failure caused or was a cause of the death of another.

In (b) above, the failure of the management in the corporation must be proven to be far below the standards that would be expected of the undertakings at the time of the fatality. The test would be based upon the law and accompanying Approved Codes of Practice, accepted industry practices, Codes of Practice and guidance. Other evidence could be in the form of safety management systems and methods of working from similar undertakings.

The prosecution would need to show that it was possible to manage the risks, by established example and, in due course, case law and precedents, that the defendant's management failed to adopt safe practices. Those unsafe acts led to a situation where serious injury or loss of life was probably inevitable. Therefore, management failed to identify the risks and control them, or they knew of the risks and failed to provide safeguards.

Involuntary Homicide Act 1995, s 4(2)

3.11 For the purposes of section 4(1) above:

(a) there is a management failure by a corporation if the way in which its activities are managed or organised fails to ensure the health and safety of persons employed in, or affected by, those activities;

(b) such a failure may be regarded as a cause of a person's death notwithstanding that the immediate cause is the act or omission of an individual.

The key issues in (a) above focuses on management failure in the way it managed or failed to manage its activities. That failure was to ensure the health and safety of its employees or persons not employed by the undertaking, but affected by the undertaking's activities. This would include but not be limited to, contractors, subcontractors, peripatetic workers, self-employed and members of the public.

In (b) above, the management failure is deemed to be the cause of death even though an individual may have done something himself and that resulted in the death of another, but the individual was acting in an official capacity within the *undertaking* at the time of the offence.

While the debate may identify that senior managers do not want to see a term of imprisonment as a punishment option, because they do not want to be in the unenviable position of facing a prison sentence for a workplace accident, a survey entitled, 'Directors respond to "corporate killer" label', showed areas of concern by directors but had the effect of providing 'fuel' to the action groups who seek greater powers for the courts to increase workplace custodial sentences.

In its review of the forthcoming corporate killing legislation, the Law Commission has identified potential weaknesses in the legal system and has recommended that there should not be scope for avoidance measures by unscrupulous companies or directors, and that enforcement action should act as a real deterrent, even in large companies and within groups of companies.

Further, it should not be possible for holding companies to attempt to evade possible liability on health and safety offences through the establishment of subsidiary companies carrying on the group's riskier business which could most readily give rise to manslaughter charges. This includes the possibility that a subsidiary company within a large group of companies might have insufficient assets to pay a large fine and that, in such cases, liability could not be transferred to its parent company. It is important that group structures should not be used as a mechanism for evasion.

The corporate killing debate continues and a major international law firm, Norton Rose, after talking to many of its clients and listening to their concerns about the Government's corporate killing proposals, commissioned an independent research report to determine the views of leading companies who would be affected by the new law.

Following publication of their report, Norton Rose organised a debate on the topic which allowed regulators, legislators and senior industry representatives to come together, under Chatham House rules, to discuss the pros and cons of the new legislation. Speaking on the panel were Frank Doran, Mike Welham, a principal inspector of the HSE, Rob Andrews of the Strategic Rail Authority and Tom Barton, deputy regional manager of contractor Sir Robert McAlpine. In the House of Commons on 30 March 2004, Aberdeen Central MP, Frank Doran set out his proposals for a Corporate Killing Bill. He told the Commons:

'My Bill would provide that a corporation would be guilty of corporate killing if management failure by that corporation was the cause, or one of the causes, of a person's death, and if that failure constituted conduct that fell far below what could reasonably be expected in the circumstances. It would also apply to a Crown body'.

The debate was held in London on Tuesday, 28 June 2004, where an audience of participants with an interest in the topic were able to put questions to the panel. The audience encompassed a wide and diverse range of industries whom, if the legislation is adopted, could find themselves at the sharp end of the corporate killing law.

According to the Norton Rose report on corporate killing, 60% of businesses thought the proposed corporate killing legislation was simply a political manoeuvre on behalf of the Government, rather than a genuine desire to improve health and safety. Gordon Hall of Norton Rose identified some of the key issues raised in the report and the debate and it is interesting and important to note that many in senior management positions believe that the only way to improve safety is to change the corporate culture from the top down, and that legislation will not significantly change people's attitudes.

There was some concern that the new offence will lead to scapegoating or witch-hunts with a focus from the media reporting following a major disaster. There was also suspicion of politicians and concern that the new law would discourage openness and drive open reporting underground. A very interesting point considered by many of the audience was that even if a company had in place robust and recognised safety systems and procedures and had been 'generally responsible', it would not protect them against being prosecuted or provide the basis of a fair trial in the face of public emotion.

It was generally recognised that there was a need for measures to deal with companies that are being negligent and escaping charges and the need to raise the profile of safety on the boardroom agenda. In the Norton Rose report, half of the industry directors contacted think the current corporate manslaughter legislation is inadequate, while a significant proportion of industry accepts that there has to be some form of new legislation.

However, there is very real concern about the lack of clarity from the Home Office as to what the law will actually mean in practice and what will constitute a grossly negligent company. This means that there will need to be some obvious criteria for judging when management conduct falls far below what is acceptable, such as the gravity of the offence and a need to examine the experience and history of the company. There would be a need to identify if there is a track record of previous health and safety offences and the responses of management to those issues and if the failings were the result of cutting corners to maximise profit.

All of these issues will require the Home Office to issue clear guidance about the law once the draft Bill is introduced.

➢ **Help point**: See 'The Norton Rose report on corporate killing – views from business'. A copy of this report and further information is available from www.nortonrose.com

Gross negligence – manslaughter

3.12 For senior management, whatever title they use, it is very important to understand that while the offence of corporate killing will encompass the undertaking, an individual could be liable for an offence in English criminal law involving deaths at, or due to, work and will be an offence of homicide.

It is beyond the scope of this book to describe in detail the criminal law of homicide which encompasses murder and manslaughter, but to provide an overview of the key elements and their status in the current criminal law. The relevance that this will have on any undertaking regarding the cost of corporate failure will extend beyond the loss of key members of the board but will have a financial loss in terms of insurance and loss of revenue.

The constituents of the Homicide Act 1957, are adequately described by JC Smith (Smith and Hogan, *Criminal Law*, (9th edn, Butterworths LexisNexis, 1999) as follows:

> 'The *actus reus* (the action of an individual) of murder and manslaughter is generally the same. It is the unlawful killing of any person 'under the Queens Peace', the death following within a year and a day. It must be proved that the defendant caused the death of the deceased person. At common law homicide was committed only if the death occurred within a year and a day of the act of causing death. That rule was abolished by the *Law Reform (Year and a Day Rule) Act 1996*. If an act *(action)* can be shown to be the cause of death, it may now be murder, or any other homicide offence, or suicide, however much time has elapsed between the act and the death. The Act, however, requires the consent of the Attorney General to the prosecution of any person for murder, manslaughter, infanticide, or any other offence of which the element is causing a person's death, or aiding and abetting suicide:
>
> (i)   where the injury alleged to have caused the death was sustained more than three years before the death occurred; or

(ii)   where the accused has previously been convicted of an offence committed in circumstances alleged to be connected with the death.'

Manslaughter is described by Smith as a complex crime of no less than five varieties. It covers three cases where the defendant kills with the fault required for murder but, because of the presence of a particular extenuating circumstance recognised by law, the offence is reduced to manslaughter. These cases are traditionally known as 'voluntary manslaughter'.

The other cases are 'involuntary manslaughter' and consist of homicides committed with a fault element less than that required for murder but recognised by the common law as sufficient to find liability for homicide.

It should be emphasised that there is only one offence. Whether the defendant is convicted of the voluntary or involuntary variety, he is convicted simply of manslaughter.

A life sentence is mandatory for murder, but for manslaughter the maximum is life, however, there is no minimum. It is an offence which may be committed with a wide variety of culpability and sometimes may be properly dealt with by a fine or a conditional or absolute discharge. The law might be summarised as follows.

A person is guilty of manslaughter where:

(a)   he kills or is a party to the killing of another with the fault required for murder but he acted:

    (i)   under diminished responsibility (Homicide Act 1957, s 2);

    (ii)   under provocation (Homicide Act 1957, s 3);

    (iii)   in pursuance of a suicide pact (Homicide Act 1957, s 4);

(b)   he is not guilty of murder by reason only of the fact that, because of voluntary intoxication, he lacked the fault required; or

(c)   he kills another:

    (i)   by an unlawful and dangerous act; or

    (ii)   being:

- grossly negligent as to death; or

- reckless as to the death or serious harm; or possibly

- grossly negligent as to serious bodily harm; or

- reckless as to any bodily harm.

A person cannot ordinarily be found guilty of a serious criminal offence unless two elements are present:

- the *actus reus* (guilty act); and

- the *mens rea* (guilty mind).

A wrongful act on its own, therefore, cannot usually be criminal unless the wrongful state of mind required for that offence is also present.

The *mens rea* for murder is malice aforethought, and that term has been made clearer through a House of Lords decision. The case of *R v Moloney [1985] HL* involved a soldier who became involved in a heated discussion with his stepfather about guns. The stepfather goaded him that he would not dare to fire a live bullet. At that point, Moloney fired a loaded gun at him and killed him.

The case focused on the definition of malice aforethought and the House of Lords determined that nothing less than the intention to kill or cause grievous bodily harm would constitute malice aforethought. Where there has been a death, but the key element of intent is missing, the offence is reduced to that of manslaughter.

In the workplace situation we are interested in manslaughter by gross negligence. This occurs where there is an act or omission of negligence that goes beyond the civil law concept of negligence. The act or omission would be so extreme that criminal liability would be the outcome. The determination of the degree of negligence is a matter of legal process through the courts (see *R v Adomako (1994)*). It will be a matter for the jury to determine the degree of negligence to identify that there was gross negligence.

Gross negligence determined in *R v Bateman (1925)* is based upon the existence of a duty of care owed by the defendant to the victim, breach of which has resulted in death, in circumstances of negligence that shows a disregard for the life and safety of others as to be deserving of a criminal sanction. In *Adomoko*, Lord MacKay LC ruled that the test for gross negligence:

> 'will depend on the seriousness of the duty, in all the circumstances in which the defendant was placed when it occurred. The jury will have to consider whether the extent to which the defendants conduct departed from the proper standard of care incumbent upon him, involving as it must have done, a risk of death to the patient, was such that it should be judged criminal'.

Imprisonment was the outcome in a case reported by Prior (Prior G, 'Construction News', May 2002) who states:

> 'Britain's first building boss found guilty of manslaughter is behind bars this week starting an 18-month stretch. The sentence will send shockwaves through the industry, as courts get tough with health and safety offenders. Brian Dean, 60, from Stoke-on-Trent, was jailed last week after being found

guilty by jury of the manslaughter of Michael and Carl Redgate. The father-and-son team died when a tunnel kiln they were demolishing collapsed in July 2000, burying them under tonnes of rubble. Sentencing Dean, Judge John Shand said: "You took on this job of demolishing a tunnel kiln when you were out of your depth. The risk of the kiln collapsing was a risk you understood and you did not warn the Redgates of this risk. Two deaths followed from this case. The least sentence I can pass is 18-months".'

The article continues to provide the views of the Construction Confederation:

'Construction Confederation health and safety director, Suzannah Nichol, said: "If this doesn't make them stand up and take notice then they don't deserve to be in the industry. The 18-month sentence show that courts can and will find directors responsible for their actions. Jailing directors has always been talked about, but this makes it a reality". Construction union leaders welcomed the sentence, which they believe will boost safety standards'.

Prosecutions of individuals for manslaughter is on the increase and whilst there are many to quote, only one has been selected because it shows the extreme failings and disregard with regard to health and safety. Reported in the *Safety and Health Practitioner* was the case of Peter Pell who was charged with manslaughter and in December 2003 received a term of imprisonment of one year.

The case involved a skid-steer loading machine which had been purchased with a safety cage and several other safety features. Pell immediately removed the cage which also made all of the other safety devices inoperable. An employee, Shaun Cooper, was using the machine when there was an incident and because there were no safety devices working he was crushed to death. This was the second death of a worker while in Pell's employment. In the first case a man was electrocuted after his truck hit overhead power lines.

It does not matter what size the undertaking is, the person at the top or the 'boss' needs to be a leader and set examples to ensure the health and safety of all employees.

Imprisonment

3.13 The majority of directors of companies or principals in partnerships, trusts and other unincorporated undertakings are law-abiding individuals. This means that they usually conduct their lives without recourse to the courts, and the criminal justice system is an alien place reserved for those who carry out criminal acts such as theft and violence.

It is considered that breaches of health and safety legislation are outside of the perceived criminal offences and, therefore, prison is not seen as an acceptable option.

Under current law, the highest sanction that is available to the courts for certain health and safety offences is imprisonment. There has throughout the years of the HSWA 1974 being in place, a reluctance by judges and juries to find a verdict that will commit an individual to prison because workplace incidents have historically been viewed as civil matters where compensation is seen as the principal legal outcome. There is, however, a change in public acceptability and the demands for imprisonment are being viewed as a viable punishment for workplace wrongdoers.

As discussed earlier, the failure to comply with a Statutory Notice is a serious disregard for health and safety and requires to be dealt with by the courts in a like manner. The seriousness is heightened when there is a failure to act upon advice provided. This leaves no defence and the sanction needs to reflect the displeasure of the legal system for such disregard.

A case that is examined is quoted from 'Safety Management', December 1999:

> 'A self-employed building developer was sentenced to four months in jail after a court heard that he failed to comply with the requirements of an improvement notice issued by the Health and Safety Executive (HSE) ... The court heard that HSE inspectors had visited the site during June and July 1998, and advised Majeed that he needed to install edge protection to prevent workers falling from heights.
>
> The inspectors also identified the need for Majeed to provide adequate welfare facilities for his workers – including running water. However, during a follow-up visit in November 1998, the inspectors found that no action had been taken to deal with the problems they had identified. In addition, they found that the protective fencing at the front and rear of the building had been removed. This meant that members of the public could easily gain access to the building and be exposed to risk.

As a result, HSE inspectors issued an improvement notice requiring Majeed to install adequate fencing at the site by 20 December 1998. The inspectors visited the site again on 22 December 1998 to check that the improvement notice had been complied with. Although they found that some of the windows in the building had been boarded up, there was still no adequate protective fencing around the site.

The inspectors also found that Majeed had failed to install suitable edge protection, which they had recommended during their earlier visits. As a result, they issued a Prohibition Notice requiring all work at height to be stopped until appropriate edge protection had been installed.

The court heard that Majeed had been fined for previous breaches of health and safety law during 1994. This included failure to comply with four Prohibition Notices and several breaches of building regulations. Abdul Majeed was sentenced to four months in jail under section 33(1) of the HSWA 1974 for failing to comply with the requirements of an improvement notice.

The seriousness of the offence in the above case was exacerbated by Majeed's previous record with breaches of notices and regulations. It does show a poor culture with regard to health and safety and, in such cases, a prison sentence would probably be the only viable option.

One of the most serious criminal acts is perverting the course of justice and those found guilty inevitably receive a custodial sentence. An example is described in 'Safety Management', February 1997 which states:

> 'Director convicted for cold and calculated attempt to pervert the course of justice: A property developer accused of covering up the cause of a fatal accident in a cold and calculated attempt to pervert the course of justice was sentenced to three months in prison and ordered to pay a fine of £12,000 ... Harper was given the jail sentence as a result of a police prosecution for attempting to pervert the course of justice. He was also fined £12,000 – and his company JK Investments £20,000 – for breaches of the Health and Safety at Work Act 1974 ... JK Investments was converting the Royal Hotel in Union Street, Dundee to flats when the accident occurred ... John Stupart was killed instantly after a gate, which had not been properly fastened to a hoist came loose and fell 40 feet, smashing Stupart's skull as he walked below'.

Harper, who pleaded not guilty to all of the charges, accused police and HSE officials of lying to frame him. Defending Harper and JK Investments, Ray Small QC told the court that Harper was not involved in the day-to-day running of the company and said that 'Harper will carry the burden of what happened for the rest of his life'.

JK Investments Limited was ordered to pay £12,500 under section 2(1) of the HSWA 1974; £5,000 under section 3(1); and £2,500 under section 42(1) of the Construction (Lifting Operations) Regulations 1961.

The firm was found not guilty of an offence under section 37(1) of HSWA 1974. Harper was ordered to pay £12,000 – the largest fine ever given to a director of a construction company in a Scottish court – under section 37(1) of HSWA 1974. Costs are not awarded in Scottish courts.

Fines and costs

3.14   A Fine is the most commonplace option for undertakings and individuals that are found guilty of health and safety offences. Companies will often argue that to be subjected to a heavy fine and costs will have a detrimental affect on the shareholders and employees. For example, when a prosecution is taken against a company for health and safety breaches and there is a plea of not guilty at the initial hearings and the company opts for trial in the Magistrates' Court. Prior to the trial date they change their plea to that of guilty and the case is presented to the magistrates where maximum fines are sought as well as full costs.

There was no mitigation in respect of the offences but the case is put by the defence that if the company were to be fined to the maximum, a number of staff would be made redundant so that the fines and costs could be paid.

The magistrates, while accepting that the case is serious, identify that it is a high unemployment area and they could not, therefore, impose maximum fines. They took the view that to do so would place people out of work who were innocent of the offences and actions of the company. Fines and costs are imposed on the company, but far less than those sought. The fact that the managing director and his son arrive at court in separate Rolls Royce cars does nothing to dispel the public view that the courts have failed to administer fair justice.

What is not known, and therefore not considered, are the salaries and bonuses paid to senior management, particularly in large undertakings. Fines imposed for health and safety breaches should not be a burden on employees, but should affect those in control. The loss of annual bonuses by all board members would focus the attitude for the future and deliver the penalty where it belongs.

The issue about fines for corporate crime is the subject of discussion by JC Smith (Smith and Hogan, *Criminal Law*, (9th edn, Butterworths LexisNexis, 1999) who states:

> 'the fine imposed is ultimately borne by the shareholders who, in most cases are not responsible, in any sense, for the offence. If they really had any control over the directors and so over management of the company, this might afford some justification; but it is generally recognized that they have no such control over large, public companies ... Since the persons actually responsible for the offence may, in the great majority of cases, be convicted, is there any need to impose this additional penalty?

> Arguments in favour of corporate liability are that there may be difficulty in fixing individuals with liability where someone among the "brains" of the corporation has undoubtedly authorised the offence. Corporate liability ensures that the offence will not go unpunished and that a fine proportionate to the gravity of the offence may be imposed, when it might be out of proportion to the means of the individuals concerned. The imposition of liability on the organisation gives all those directing it an interest in the

prevention of illegalities, and they are in a position to prevent them, though the shareholders are not'.

It is not only shareholders who see fines imposed for health and safety offences, but there are the undertakings who provide a vital service to the public, which identifies implications of heavy fines. The case shown is that of a health care trust, which was fined £38,000 plus £17,000 costs.

The trust admitted that it failed to take the necessary steps to ensure the safe control of all stages of cardiac angiography procedures. As a consequence, a patient died after being injected with air instead of radio-opaque fluid during a routine cardiac angiography. The case highlights the need for the healthcare sector to manage health and safety at work properly, just like any other employer.

The resulting investigation showed that it was not a failure of the equipment of itself, but a failure of the management to implement a safe system of work to deliver clinical judgement, which caused this tragic and avoidable death. In passing sentence the judge identified that the case was important because it raised issues not present in other cases concerning prosecutions of National Health Service trusts. The failure in this case was the absence of a safe system of work to protect patients and employees, which arose from the use of this equipment.

The case was heard in the Magistrates' Court but sent to the Crown Court for sentence where the level of fine is unlimited. The lawyer representing the National Health Service (NHS) trust told the court that every pound that the hospital is fined is a pound less spent on the care of our community.

This evidence shows that there is a need to avoid placing a debit upon the innocent shareholders and employees and means that there has to be alternative penalty options. The level of fines imposed for health and safety offences are deemed to be low and has for some time been an area of concern for both the Health and Safety Commission (HSC) and exponents who claim that there is a failing in the level of penalties, for all health and safety prosecutions.

Another interesting point is raised by Celia Wells in *Corporations and Criminal Responsibility* (Oxford University Press (2001)) who puts forward the argument that both Magistrates' and Crown Courts frequently require social reports to be prepared for individuals, as well as the completion of a personal means form prior to sentencing. However, with corporate defendants, there is generally no attempt made to investigate the financial background or assets, before imposing fines.

Alternatives to fines

3.15   A major question raised by numerous commentators and focus groups with regard to punishment of undertakings for health and safety failures is that if financial penalties do not deter management, what options are possible that will? The Health and Safety Commission's 'Revitalising Health and Safety Strategy' commits it to looking for 'innovative' penalties that could be added to the penalty options. Many of the possible options are already in the criminal law system and deflect from financial penalties, which can impact on shareholders, the public and employees, and direct the penalty to personal liability.

Directors' disqualification

3.16   The courts do have the option to disqualify directors, although it is rarely used. A case reported in 'Health and Safety' November 1998 provides details.

'Company director disqualified after employee accident

A man has been disqualified from being a company director for five years, after one of his employees was severely injured by an unguarded machine ... an emergency call had been made at the premises of Rainham Waste Recycling Ltd in Essex. An employee, Ali Taofiq, was caught in the prop shaft driving a wood-chipping machine, and was only freed when his left arm came off. His neck was broken, paralysing him from the chest down and preventing movement in his right hand.

The decision was taken to prosecute the Managing Director, Tony O'Sullivan, personally, because the firm was small enough for him "to know exactly what was going on" in the factory. Section 37 of the Health and Safety at Work etc Act 1974 enables prosecution of an individual. whose consent, connivance or neglect has allowed an offence to be committed.

O'Sullivan and Rainham Waste pleaded guilty to breaching Regulation 11(1) of the Provision and Use of Work Equipment Regulations 1992 by failing to guard dangerous machinery. On 24 September, Snaresbrook Crown Court fined O'Sullivan £5,000 and his company £25,000 with costs of £4,000.

The Company Directors Disqualification Act 1986 was used to disqualify O'Sullivan. This Act was intended to crack down on fraud, but the HSE has used it eight times for safety offences. Hodges hoped the case "gives a clear message to directors that ultimately they are responsible for health and safety and can be held personally liable."'

Directors' bonus

3.17   Many businesses make a reward to the senior management for reaching corporate targets, generally focused on turnover and profit. It is, for many, the driver for senior management to meet corporate objectives. In many cases, the reward is linked to the targets that are reached and are personal motivators.

In the case of a corporate failure in health and safety, where the consequences are fatalities, serious accidents or risks to the health of others there is the potential option of prohibiting director bonuses for a fixed period which, in some cases with senior executives of large corporations, can be a substantial figure.

The question would be as to who would carry the burden. This could be answered by identifying the board of directors or equivalent in unincorporated undertakings and delivering the penalty to all at that level as they are all representatives of the 'corporate' body. They reap the rewards of profit, they should share the burden of failure. This option could be introduced to encourage senior management to take a greater interest and participation in health and safety.

Suspending management

3.18   Where individual managers are found to have failed, the option of suspending those individuals without pay may be effective. This would encourage management below director level who may disregard health and safety in their operational decisions in order to get the job done for some form of personal gain. This style of option has been proven to be an effective penalty as in a situation that did not reach court but which involved a manager who ignored health and safety considerations for financial gain.

The manager was responsible for an operation that was being carried out for a fixed sum of money. He had a completion bonus that was linked to meeting the budget. When the job ran over the limit his bonus reduced quite rapidly. He was, therefore, under 'personal gain' pressure to complete the operation on time. As the job progressed he identified a situation where corners could be cut to the detriment to employees. He directed a change in the programme where the outcome was a failure in the equipment and by shear luck the employee was not injured. The consequences were such that any injury would have been fatal.

An HSE inspector, having investigated the incident, encouraged the company to impose a serious sanction on the manager. This was achieved by the removal of all bonuses which amounted to several thousand pounds and he was suspended from his post until he had undertaken and passed an accredited health and safety training course.

This was a new course of action and it saved regulatory time and expensive enforcement against the undertaking, which, in this case, was not at fault, but held the ultimate duty under the HSWA 1974. Under the circumstances, enforcement action had been a viable option, but the message it sent to boardroom was to review its bonus policy. It delivered an effective message to the manager who lost financially along with personal credibility. In the wider sense, it sent a strong message to all managers for the need to conform to corporate procedures and not embark on frolics of their own.

Suspended sentences

3.19   The option of 'suspended sentences' pending remedial actions avoids a repetition of the breach. This means that the undertaking or individuals are not punished at the time, but the sentence that would have been imposed would be suspended for a pre-determined time of, for example, eighteen months, during which time if there were further breaches of health and safety legislation, the undertaking or individual would return to court and be sentenced for the new offence as well as the original sentence that had been suspended.

The HSE and local authority inspectors already have an effective tool available in the form of Prohibition and Improvement Notices, which require remedial actions.

Failure to comply with a notice can result in imprisonment, and it is a matter for the courts to understand the seriousness of such notices and the failure to comply and impose effective sanctions including, if appropriate, custody.

Compulsory health and safety training

3.20   Another option identified by the strategy is to impose compulsory health and safety training where there has been a health and safety failure. This is a valid option, which is raised by Peter Rogerson ('Health and safety sentencing – a better way?' *Magistrate Magazine*, Summer 2002) whose case is:

> 'Health and safety offences are generally dealt with by way of fines and remedy orders ... This will usually reflect the seriousness of the offence, the degree of co-operation of the company concerned, the warnings given, the

timeliness of the plea and the size of the resources of the organisation ... specific charges are now often accompanied by additional charges of general failure under the Management of Health and Safety at Work Regulations 1992 to undertake suitable risk assessments ... But is this approach, particularly when dealing with small and medium enterprises, fulfilling the primary objective of the court, which is to prevent re-offending. Will a fine on the company or its management necessarily make the working environment any safer for its workers and visitors alike? Why do businesses commit health and safety offences?

Clearly there are those driven by profit and greed. Such companies, quite rightly, deserve to be hit hard with the full weight of the law and often end up in the Crown Court for sentencing. Most, however, commit offences because of poor management, lack of resources, ignorance and confusion ... we could look to other areas for inspiration. Courts are now able to direct offenders through the probation service to undertake training on alcohol awareness, anger management and drug abuse to name but a few ... Can this principle be applied to companies and directors who commit health and safety offences?

At the lower end the smaller organisations could have a health and safety training order, where, instead of a significant fine, the company, the company would be required to send the executive named by the court (usually its most senior executive, director, partner or proprietor) on approved health and safety management training course. Such a course could be one or two days and failure to comply would result in significant fines both for the company. Medium size companies could be given a health and safety training and action plan order, where, in addition to the training, the company would be required to work with an approved consultant ... for a specified time ... with the aim of creating a safety management system and instilling a "safety culture"'.

This option is commendable in its concept but does highlight some major hurdles. In particular, what type of health and safety training could be adopted? Is a one or two-day training course a suitable option as opposed to a £20,000 fine. The question can be asked as to what and whose course would be deemed suitable, who would be the training provider and who would attend? Equally important is the question of consultants and their competence levels and, if they fail to provide suitable and sufficient information to their clients, should they be ordered to undertake training?

Community Punishment Orders

3.21 There is the option of considering the use of Community Punishment Orders, such as those already used in the criminal courts. This requires an individual to undertake unpaid work in the community at large for a pre-determined period of time. Such an option may be useful where an appropriate fine would plunge a company into financial difficulties. The question arises as to who would physically carry out any such order, particularly where there were several directors, partners or trustees. It is claimed that such orders could enhance the company's image in the community, with those undertaking work wearing corporate overalls or other protective clothing advertising their organisation. Such orders could result in the work being carried out by innocent employees.

This option has some advantages, but would require 'loopholes' to be plugged, because it can be anticipated that many of those who breach health and safety law, will not be averse to breaching punishment orders. It is a trend in the general criminal process and would easily roll over to the commercial world.

The proposal is for courts to have the power to impose Community Service Orders (now called a Community Punishment Order) to replace, either in part or in full, a fine. Any such order must be punitive as it is replacing a fine, the latter having a negative effect on the company. The cost of community service would be borne by the company with the rehabilitative element being seen to give something back to the community. Any such order should not require the consent of the convicted company prior to imposing the sentence because it would provide too convenient a refuge for corporations wishing to pay fines rather than suffer a more severe type of sentence. The calculation of the value of the community service would include the cost of materials and labour and not the number of hours, as is the case with conventional criminal orders. Corporate orders would have to be subject to a completion period which is would be a two-year period.

The type of community service imposed upon an individual organisation would be dependant upon the skills and resources available and, where possible, have some relationship to the offence that had been committed. It will be important that any project should involve the senior management of the undertaking and not be a burden to those at a lower level. There may be situations where other expertise would need to be brought into the project, and that would be encompassed within the financial restraints of the Community Punishment Order. The profile of any order will need to be within the means and capabilities of the undertaking.

There will need to be a requirement for the offender to prepare a report before it commences community service, which sets out the plan of how the undertaking will comply with the Community Punishment Order. The court will need to appoint an independent person to provide advice on the suitability of the plan. Upon completion of the Community Punishment Order, a report should be prepared providing details of the work carried out so as to advise the court of completion of the order. If an undertaking completes the specified work in the allocated time frame to a satisfactory standard, then it will have met its obligations. If the undertaking fails to comply with the order, the court can revoke the Community Punishment

Order and fine the undertaking up to one-and-a-half times the original amount of the fine.

There are other commentators expressing views on corporate Community Punishment Orders, such as that portrayed by Gary Slapper and Steve Tombs in *Corporate Crime* (Pearson Education, 1999) where they quote:

> '... soup kitchens for the homeless if it had previously sold adulterated food; sending its executives to do voluntary work in emergency rooms if they deliberately built cars that became fire bombs when hit from the rear; or requiring its board to work in Veterans Administration hospitals if the corporation profited from systematically falsifying test records on drugs, declaring them safe when they were not'.

Clearly the adoption of Community Service Orders is an option for the courts as a corporate punishment, however, there are some fundamental flaws in the concept that would need to be addressed and will be addressed in the conclusions. Employees carrying out work could see themselves being identified as being criminals whilst senior management remained in their offices away from the eyes of the public.

Company probation orders

3.22   A further option would be the use of company probation orders. The adoption of such orders, proponents claim, could facilitate rehabilitation by forcing immediate changes in the company's decision-making, monitoring and personal incentive processes. This raises the important question as to who will undertake the planning and supervision. It would be expensive to operate and would it focus on those who have the ultimate control because companies are often diverse and fragmented in their structure, particularly with large enterprises? This option extends to deterring companies by barring a company from particular business activities. This enters another realm when courts that may not have the knowledge and expertise of corporate law could be expected to make decisions that result in a business failing, with all of the consequences that could entail. This also raises issues under the Human Rights Act 1998, because restricting business operations could affect the operating viability of an undertaking.

Corporate probation orders would be an amended version of probation orders imposed on individuals in the criminal courts. The focus of such order should be rehabilitative in nature but be seen by the public to be an effective punishment. Probation orders are generally imposed as an alternative to a custodial sentence but, as an undertaking cannot be sent to prison, such an order should be imposed in addition to a cash or equity fine.

Fixed penalty notices

3.23　Another options is that of fixed penalty notices for specific offences coupled with a penalty point system modelled on the driver's licence system. Occupational health and safety is a complex subject affecting undertakings involved in diverse activities and of varying sizes. Breaches of health and safety law are often based on an inspector's interpretation at the time of an inspection. The inspector would have to make a judgement on the spot and issue a fixed penalty notice. The management of the company would have the right of appeal.

In comparison, a speeding offence is committed and evidence proves it, either by a fixed or mobile camera. There is a defined speed limit, the breach of which is calculated by the excess speed. The penalty notice is issued and, in the majority of cases, the fine is paid.

The issue of penalty points in driving cases is straightforward in concept because there is a licence and data system to administer it in place. Organisations come and go and there is no registration scheme for business or industry. This would make for an administrative failure or if a system was adopted, an administrative burden.

Penalty points

3.24　The report proposes the introduction of penalty points for health and safety offences. This means that if a company is convicted of a serious health and safety offence(s), a company director should receive penalty points. These would need to be officially recorded through an endorsement on the company's registration form. While such a system could be adopted for limited companies, consideration would need to be given to extending it to partnerships, trusts and self employed persons.

The proposal would be based upon the following concept:

- where a company director is found to be guilty of an offence listed below, the court must endorse the company registration form, with a number of penalty points which are attributable to each offence committed;

- the number of penalty points which the court should attribute to any offence is:

    (a)　the number; or

    (b)　where a range of numbers is shown, a number within the range;

- any penalty points endorsed onto the company registration form as a result of the conviction of a director should count as the penalty points for that director alone.

Equity fines

3.25 Courts should have the power to impose 'equity fines' on limited companies. This would involve the court ordering a company to issue a specified number of shares, valued at a particular price, and place them into a fund. A court should only be able to impose an equity fine when two situations exist:

(a) the company must be a public limited company; and

(b) the courts should have assessed that the company might not pay the cash fine without passing the amount onto its workers or customers.

The basis of any proposal would be as outlined below.

- *Court power to impose an equity fine* – when a court is sentencing a public limited company, and it has reasonable cause to believe that if it sentenced the company to a cash fine there would be unreasonable consequences on the company's employees or there is a real risk of bankruptcy, the court may sentence the company to an equity fine.

- *Ordering a company to issue shares to court* – when sentencing a company to an equity fine, the court shall order the company to issue shares, equal in sum to the cash fine that the court would otherwise impose on the company, into a fund set up by the court.

Health and safety insurance cover

3.26 The insurance industry is carrying the commercial burden for incidents at work and there is growing evidence that part of their review into accidents indicates that the subsequent civil claim settlements are increasing. To counter this cover for risk activities, the insurance industry is contracting with fewer underwriters to service the employer's liability insurance cover. This is resulting in a greater scrutiny of those being covered. The outcome is increased premiums, in many cases quite heavy increases and, in a growing number of cases, those businesses carrying a perceived risk are being refused cover regardless of premium cost. The continuation of a change in the insurance industry will mean business will face serious operational problems in the legal sense in that that 'no insurance means no business'.

The insurance industry is now looking more closely at the risks it will underwrite and directors involved in high-risk industries may well have experienced a review with their insurers in order that the insurers can fully understand the measures the company has in place to protect its employees and assets. This will include a review of the company's safety performance. The meeting is usually conducted on an annual basis and, in recent years, the questions have become more probing.

Federation of Small Businesses survey

3.27　　As reported by the Federation of Small Businesses in a survey conducted in June 2003 with regard to insurance, 20% of employers in the survey of more than 1,000 small businesses claimed to have laid off employees or put a freeze on recruitment as a result of escalating premiums. One in five firms reported they were facing a doubling of premiums on top of previous increases.

The report also indicates that a quarter of employees found it impossible to find employers liability insurance at any price despite it being a legal requirement in the UK and, worryingly, 8% of those surveyed were trading without the compulsory cover. The report stated that 32% of the respondents had shown an interest in health and safety records, rising to 38% if they had transferred to a new insurer.

The report suggests there is little incentive for small businesses to demonstrate their health and safety record if it is not taken into consideration by the vast majority of insurers. This is an interesting comment, but if a director has to review his business risks with his insurers, then, from experience of the reviews, it is not an easy discussion even when a business has a proactive positive safety culture and good safety record.

Revitalising Health and Safety strategy

3.28　　The HSE's Revitalising Health and Safety initiative promotes the message that 'Good Health and Safety is Good Business'. With regard to the impact of a poor claims record on insurance premiums the HSE quotes the following example.

An insurance company became seriously concerned over a foundry with an increasing claims record. They organised a health and safety survey of the foundry. This showed:

(a)　　high levels of noise not fully appreciated by the company;

(b)　　the wearing of hearing protection not adequately enforced;

(c)　　no noise control measures in place other than hit and miss use of hearing protection;

(d)   no statutory examinations of plant and equipment being done;

(e)   the foundry had been prosecuted for health and safety breaches and substantially fined;

(f)   health and safety documents were sparse and disorganised;

(g)   employees had developed an insurance claims culture;

(h)   managers appeared to have lost control of health and safety management.

The insurance company considered withdrawing cover. After a meeting with the foundry's board of directors, insurance cover was continued. This was subject to:

(i)   a 100% increase to employers liability insurance (from £100,000 to £200,000);

(ii)   mandatory involvement of the insurers health and safety team;

(iii)   the foundry paying for two days' health and safety consultancy per month for a 12-month period;

(iv)   a situation review after 12months.

If satisfactory improvements were not made within the year, insurance cover would be withdrawn.

Even where insurance cover is in place, the uninsured costs can be high. A study into a cheque-clearing department of a financial institution (a lower risk environment) found the insured against uninsured ratio to be 1:3.3. That means that for every £1 recoverable from insurance the company had to find a further £3.30 themselves. It is obvious, therefore, that the cost of poor health and safety can be high. The cost of the *Piper Alpha* disaster, which killed 167, was estimated at £2 billion. Accidents in construction can account for 3–6% of total project costs.

On a positive note to demonstrate that good safety is good business theme, one example is that of a water utility who following privatisation recognised the need for greater investment in health and safety and that the introduction of a strong health and safety culture would contribute to profitability. The company introduced a new health and safety management system in 1991. In 1991/92 there were 136 accidents per 1,000 employees. This had declined to 53 accidents per 1,000 employees by 1995/96. Using industry-wide representative costs for an accident, the water utility calculated it had saved £2,546,000 through its accident prevention measures over the period April 1992 to March 1998.

Insurance against liability

3.29 With certain specified exceptions, an employer carrying on business in Great Britain is required to insure against liability for injury or disease to any employee, arising out of, and in the course of, his/her employment in Great Britain, in that business. Changes in employment practices have resulted in problems for the insurance industry. Smaller companies employ a much higher proportion of the workforce and subcontracting has become much more common.

> 'The principle of using the insurance industry to penalise bad performance and reward good performance in companies' health and safety practices was initially thought to be sound. ... if a company finds its insurance premiums raised as a result of poor health and safety performance it can simply approach a different insurance company, which is often willing to undercut the original quote. However, the evidence now appears to show a tide-change and the insurance industry is adopting a more critical view of providing cover'.

Sanctions that will impose themselves involve insurance. Employers' liability insurance is compulsory for all employers and there is a need to have liability insurance for those who are not employed but can be affected by the undertaking. Insurance companies are already imposing restrictions on undertakings through dramatically increasing premiums. Businesses that carry risks to employees and/or others not employed, face premium increases of 40% to 60%, and in a growing number of instances, an inability to obtain cover at any cost.

The Hazards Campaign, which is a network of resource centres and campaigners on health and safety at work, proposes that companies should publish their record on health and safety and publish the name of their insurers, to prevent them from evading the requirement of having employers liability insurance and to make it easier for those seeking injury or illness compensation.

Employer's Liability (Compulsory Insurance) Act 1969

3.30 Since 1975, the HSE has been the enforcing authority for the Employer's Liability (Compulsory Insurance) Act 1969, otherwise referred to as the ELCIA 1969. The field of responsibility includes premises allocated to local authority's for HSWA 1974 enforcement as well as premises normally inspected by the HSE.

Under the ELCIA 1969 employers are obliged to:

- issue against liability for injury or disease to an employee arising out of and in the course of his or her employment in Great Britain;

- display the certificate of insurance at his or her places of business;

- produce the certificate or send a copy when required to do so by an authorised inspector;

- send the certificate or copy in response to a notice served on behalf of the HSE;

- permit an authorised inspector to inspect his policy or copy, provided that reasonable notice has been given.

With certain specified exceptions, an employer carrying on business in Great Britain is required to insure against liability for injury or disease to any employee, arising out of, and in the course of, his or her employment in Great Britain in that business. The principle of using the insurance industry to penalise bad performance and reward good performance in companies' health and safety practices was initially thought to be sound.

However, it has been shown that where a company finds its insurance premiums raised as a result of poor health and safety performance, it can simply approach a different insurance company which is often willing to undercut the original quote.

As an outcome of numerous large insurance claims in recent years, the insurance underwriters have begun to review their client base in terms of risk liability. This is coupled with the fact that the number of underwriters providing cover for employers liability insurance has dramatically reduced. These factors are having an impact on business where 'risk' is having a direct effect on premiums with dramatic increases in premiums and, in a growing number of cases, businesses are unable to obtain cover at any cost.

Another factor that will impact on premiums is the proposal that hospitals will charge for treatment where there is a workplace incident.

NHS injury at work costs

3.31 Another suggestion is that companies should pay hospital bills for workplace injuries in line with the costs recovered following a road accident where there is a liability to pay for ambulance transport and emergency NHS treatment. A study undertaken by the Health Department's economists found that employer liability for accidents and diseases and public liability for accidents are the most common types of personal injury claim. This means that the taxpayer is subsidising the medical treatment for these accidents.

The study identified that the estimated amount that could be recovered by hospitals each year for employers' liability for accidents is an estimated

£42m for in-patient treatment, £12m for outpatient treatment and £4m cost of emergency ambulance transport. It is considered that the public (local authority) liability for accidents will generate similar figures. It was concluded that it would be difficult to quantify the costs of work-related diseases due to the complexities of treatment and time frames, and this area would require further study as would the identification of types of accidents.

In a bid to recover the considerable costs of accidents and incidents the study proposed the following:

- Introduce, through primary legislation, the recovery of charges parasitic on payment of compensation based on a simple tariff system of NHS charges with central collection by the Department of Work and Pensions Compensation recovery Unit.

- The adoption of the proposal would generate finance for the NHS in excess of £100m per year from liable parties. This does not include money recovered from road accident costs.

- The proposal would affect any business, which has potential liabilities for personal injury, which can be an employer, a producer of goods or the undertaking business in a public place. This will impact on insurance companies who will have to apportion costs to clients, as they will face a recovery of costs bill estimated to be in the region of £100m to £120m. Where insurance is not compulsory, it is anticipated that responsible businesses will carry insurance cover, such as contractor's all-risk insurance, which includes an element of public liability cover.

The consultation document identified that:

'The vast majority of businesses in the United Kingdom employ fewer than 50 people and are therefore classed as small businesses. More than two thirds of these small businesses are sole proprietorships and partnerships comprising only the self-employed owner manager(s) and comprising only an employee director … Where any business is run on a tight margin the impact of any increase in either compulsory or voluntary insurance premiums will be unwelcome. However, the small business attracts responsibilities for the safety and well being of people who come into contact with it in just the same way as any other business and should be encouraged to both reduce that risk wherever possible and to make sensible and prudent provision for meeting the costs of any accidents should they nevertheless occur'. ['The recovery of National Health Service Costs in Cases Involving Personal Injury Compensation: A Consultation', Department of Health, September 2002.]

The Government is keen to recover the medical treatment costs created by business incidents and in 'Safety Management', October 2002, Health Minister David Lammy stated:

> 'This scheme will not introduce any more regulations for business but it is unacceptable that taxpayers have to pay for the medical treatment of someone injured at work simply because employers fail to take adequate steps to protect their workforce. By having to bear the cost of treating those injured in the workplace, employers will have another incentive to reduce risks to their workforce and the public at large. People have a right to treatment free at the point of entry to the NHS. Employers have a responsibility to reduce the possibility of accidents to their workers'.

If the proposal is adopted, it will have an impact on the insurance market which will cascade to those who carry insurance cover. This is because a hospital will charge the employer or appropriate body for treatment which will have to be covered by insurance. This will result in an increase in insurance premiums, which will be in addition to the dramatic increases already faced by businesses. There are potential consequences in that undertakings that are required to carry insurance cover will not do so, leaving those injured covered by medical treatment, but with the NHS unable to recover costs.

The imposition that higher insurance premiums to cover NHS costs should encourage undertakings to review health and safety management systems and risk control measures is a positive move and there will need to be effective measures for dealing with those who do not have insurance cover or are unable to pay direct.

The cost of failure

3.32   This chapter aimed to summarise the cost of failure both at director and company level. A recent case reported in the Aberdeen *Press and Journal* on September 13 2003, describes safety failures as being treated seriously by the courts. Paul Timson, trading as Nixon Industrial Valves and VSL Valve Products Ltd, was jailed for 15 months for breaches of the Health and Safety at Work etc Act 1974 for selling faulty parts to the offshore oil and gas industry. He was manufacturing ball valves and not subjecting them to standard industry working and safety tests. He then forged test certificates to fool companies into believing they were compliant with operating and safety limits.

Timson admitted 19 charges of forging safety certificates for ball valves, one charge of using forged business documents for financial gain and three charges of supplying unsafe valves. Health and safety experts considered there was a chance of a similar incident to that of *Piper Alpha* if one of the valves had failed on site.

Failure to adopt and follow health and safety legal requirements continues to impact on those who flaunt them. The ultimate sanction for blatant disregard is custody but there are other sanctions being proposed, all of which would have detrimental affect on undertakings and those who manage them. The message is simple: management must be proactive and set the standards through positive leadership.

Chapter 4

Corporate Governance – the Link to Health and Safety

Introduction

4.0   This chapter sets the scene for the objectives of the book, which is to focus on the management of health and safety in the workplace through leadership and trust. It is recognised that there are undertakings where health and safety is an integral part of the culture, and those undertakings will understand the benefits. However, there are many more undertakings where there is no culture and health and safety is an 'add-on' – if adopted at all.

In those undertakings there may be management but there is no leadership and probably no trust by the employees working within that undertaking. There are many senior managers who claim that when things are going well that health and safety is a key factor in their undertaking. However, when things go wrong and there is 'blood on the floor' then it is somebody else's fault or problem. A prime objective is to encourage management from the boardroom to supervisory level to belong to the first class and do so through leadership that encompasses a climate of trust within the undertaking. The classic statement that was made by Mr Justice Sheen in 1987 in his enquiry into the management of P&O European Ferries Ltd following the *Herald of Free Enterprise* disaster. He stated:

> 'from top to bottom the body corporate was infected with the disease of sloppiness ... The failure on the part of the shore management to give proper and clear directions was a contributory cause of the disaster'.

Health and safety at work is one of those topics that evokes differing reactions from people. Often, when confronted, all levels of staff and management in an undertaking will react to the need to conduct their activities safely or to attend health and safety training with a negative response. This is, of course, a quite irrational reaction as health and safety issues are a positive, yet often it receives a negative. That applies until there is an accident, and then it is everybody else's problem apart from those involved. It follows that sometimes there is an individual in an undertaking who considers health and safety important and promotes the subject, but they are ridiculed as a 'time waster', a 'softy' and someone who wants to spend money on something that is unnecessary and a potential burden on the undertaking.

The outcome, sadly, results in such enthusiasm being buried. It is said that people do not go to work or undertake workplace activities with the intention of injuring or killing another person. Well, if they did, and it could be proved that it was an intention, then it would be murder. While the situation may not be as severe as the highest criminal offence, there are many incidents resulting from management failure which leaves workers and others affected by a workplace activities seriously injured or even killed. The tragedy is that those failings could be designed out of any undertaking – large, medium or small.

The Health and Safety at Work etc Act 1974

4.1 The Health and Safety at Work etc Act 1974 (HSAW 1974) emanated from a committee of six, chaired by Lord Robens who was chairman of the National Coal Board from 1961 until 1972. During that time, he had taken to writing personal letters to the widows and mothers of those killed in the pits. While he was chairman, deaths at work reduced in number, but he considered that there were still too many accidents. This first-hand knowledge and experience provided him with the credentials needed to chair the committee.

The Robens Committee determined that there was a need to move away from prescriptive legislation to adopting a self-regulating system which focused on the need to have better systems of safety organisation, management initiatives and more involvement of the workforce. The emphasis was that with health and safety, good management should be normal management, and that effective management will encompass detailed policy and objectives within an effective organisation.

An undertaking's structure encompasses the main board directors, executives or others identified as being in control of the organisation, the so-called 'controlling mind' (see **2.3** above). It follows that every company should have a safety management system, which should be an integrated part of the company's day-to-day activities. This will enable management to encompass health and safety within its activities providing a seamless system to ensure the safety and health of all its employees and those of its subcontractors. The emphasis being that health and safety must be equal to all other business functions such as finance, manufacturing and marketing.

It is recognised that businesses not only vary in size and complexity, but also vary by industry and even by constitution. This means that there will be varying hazards that can affect those employed as well as those who are not employed, such as contractors or members of the public.

It is, therefore, the responsibility of those at board level that set the policy and standards of the organisation to create a safe working environment. This is achieved, in part, by identifying the hazards, controlling the risks and monitoring the effectiveness of their control procedures. Responsibility for health and safety lies with the board or its equivalent, and there are case histories to support this.

Health and Safety Strategy Statement

4.2   In the 'Revitalising Health and Safety Strategy Statement' issued in June 2000, the Government stated that it would seek an early legislative opportunity, when Parliamentary time allows, to provide the courts with greater sentencing powers for health and safety crimes (the document can be found at www.hse.gov.uk/revitalising/strategy.pdf).

The key measures to be addressed include extending the £20,000 maximum fine in the lower courts to a much wider range of offences which currently attract a maximum penalty of £5,000. It is also proposed to provide the courts with the power to imprison individuals for most health and safety offences.

It was stated that the Health and Safety Executive (HSE) would monitor and draw public attention to trends in prosecution, convictions and penalties imposed by the courts by publishing a special annual report. This has been implemented and provides a database on the HSE website (www.hse.gov.uk). The objective is to 'name and shame' companies and individuals convicted in the previous twelve months by making the information available on the website.

In expanding the discussion, the consultation document stated that the Government was considering whether to make imprisonment available to the courts for all health and safety offences, and whether the maximum fine for breaches on summary conviction should be increased for offences under the HSWA 1974.

The overwhelming view of consultees was that the general level of penalties imposed by the courts is inadequate: only 7% considered that the current framework for penalties was satisfactory. Many also argued that more publicity needed to be secured for successful prosecutions. In the light of future trends in sentencing, the Government will consider a referral of health and safety offences to the independent Sentencing Advisory Panel.

Mr Lawrie Quinn MP has introduced a Parliamentary ten-minute Bill, the Health and Safety at Work (Offences) Bill, which would increase the maximum fines and make imprisonment more widely available in the Magistrates' Court. The Bill would also increase the penalty for the main offence under the Employers' Liability (Compulsory Insurance) Act 1969, and extend the time limit for bringing prosecutions for such an offence. Although the text of the Bill has not been finalised, the main proposals include:

> '[to] raise the cap on the level of fines for breaches of almost all health and safety laws to £20,000; extend the possible punishment of prison to almost all breaches of health and safety law (currently only breaches of a few sections of the Health and Safety at Work etc Act 1974 are punishable by imprisonment); and significantly increase the fine for not having a valid employer liability insurance policy, as required by the 1969 Act, to £20,000 (with provision for easy subsequent up-rating) and extend the period of time during which criminal proceedings can be brought'.

The proposal had its second reading in the House in February 2003 and there appeared to be no opposition. It is of concern that a major and fundamental change to health and safety law is the subject of a Private Members Bill and not a positive step on behalf of the Government to raise the profile of health and safety within the UK.

The draft Health and Safety at Work (Offences) Bill provides for the following options.

Item	Offence	Mode of trial	Penalty on summary conviction	Penalty on conviction on indictment
1	An offence under s 33(1)(a) consisting of the failure of a person to discharge a duty to which he is subject by virtue of s 2–6	Either way	Imprisonment for a term not exceeding six months, a fine not exceeding £20,000, or both	Imprisonment for a term not exceeding two years, a fine, or both
2	An offence under s 33(1)(a) consisting of the failure of a person to discharge a duty to which he is subject by virtue of s 7	Either way	Imprisonment for a term not exceeding six months, a fine not exceeding the statutory maximum, or both	Imprisonment for a term not exceeding two years, a fine, or both

Item	Offence	Mode of trial	Penalty on summary conviction	Penalty on conviction on indictment
3	An offence under s 33(1)(b) consisting of a contravention of s 8	Either way	Imprisonment for a term not exceeding six months, a fine not exceeding £20,000, or both	Imprisonment for a term not exceeding two years, a fine, or both
4	An offence under s 33(1)(b) consisting of a contravention of s 9	Either way	A fine not exceeding £20,000	A fine
5	An offence under s 33(1)(c)	Either way	Imprisonment for a term not exceeding six months, a fine not exceeding £20,000, or both	Imprisonment for a term not exceeding two years, a fine, or both
6	An offence under s 33(1)(d)	Summary only	A fine not exceeding level 5 on the standard scale	
7	An offence under s 33(1)(e), (f) or (g)	Either way	Imprisonment for a term not exceeding six months, a fine not exceeding £20,000, or both	Imprisonment for a term not exceeding two years, a fine, or both
8	An offence under s 33(1)(h)	Summary only	Imprisonment for a term not exceeding six months, a fine not exceeding level 5 on the standard scale, or both	
9	An offence under s 33(1)(i)	Either way	A fine not exceeding the statutory maximum	A fine

Item	Offence	Mode of trial	Penalty on summary conviction	Penalty on conviction on indictment
10	An offence under s 33(1)(j)	Either way	Imprisonment for a term not exceeding six months, a fine not exceeding the statutory maximum, or both	Imprisonment for a term not exceeding two years, a fine, or both
11	An offence under s 33(1)(k), (l) or (m)	Either way	Imprisonment for a term not exceeding six months, a fine not exceeding £20,000, or both	Imprisonment for a term not exceeding two years, a fine, or both
12	An offence under s 33(1)(n)	Summary only	A fine not exceeding level 5 on the standard scale	
13	An offence under s 33(1)(o)	Either way	Imprisonment for a term not exceeding six months, a fine not exceeding £20,000 or both	Imprisonment for a term not exceeding two years, a fine, or both
14	An offence under any of the existing statutory provisions, being an offence for which no other penalty is specified	Either way	Imprisonment for a term not exceeding six months, a fine not exceeding £20,000, or both	Imprisonment for a term not exceeding two years, a fine or both

> **Help point:** It is clearly evident that there is a determined focus on proactive action against senior managers through punitive punishments on the undertakings they represent. Senior management can be proactive and reduce potential liabilities.

Corporate governance

4.3 During the 1980s, Polly Peck, BCCI and Robert Maxwell's Mirror Group News International were all victims of poorly managed business practices that led to failure of those companies. Amid the concern of such failures, the Cadbury Committee was established by the UK Stock Exchange. The membership of the committee represented representatives from the senior level of British industry. Their task was to develop a code of practice that would provide guidance in defining and applying internal controls to limit the risks of financial loss whatever the cause. While the effects of serious accidents were not specified, there would be losses and the consequences would be financial as a result of management failure.

The committee produced a report in 1992 and a Code of Best Practice. The recommendations of the code were not mandatory, but all UK quoted companies listed on the UK stock exchange must now clearly state whether or not the Code has been followed, and if it has not, then they had to explain why. The report focused on corporate governance by identifying that there was a need for a clearly accepted division of responsibilities at the head of a company. The objective was to ensure a balance of power and authority, such that no individual had unfettered power of decision.

The foundation of the report was on the role of directors, both in their boardroom function and as individuals. It identified a need to introduce risk management hrough reporting and control measures. Risk management was not identified as an official duty for directors, however, there is a requirement for board members to include a formal statement confirming compliance with the code, which raises the profile of risk management overall.

A key objective of the code was to make directors and non-executive directors aware of the need for boardroom confirmation that their companies are protected from major losses resulting from inappropriate working practices. A problem that was identified in obtaining full support from the boardroom was that it was generally considered that risk management was linked to insurance. This was a situation that had to be addressed, as boardroom members could not absolve their responsibilities to a third-party 'safety net'.

There are three key points for risk management: identification, evaluation and control, which encompass all aspects of corporate activities and that includes safety management. Hazards need to be identified and controlled with an audit system to identify compliance, all as an integrated part of a safety management system. The code should place full responsibility for health and safety within a corporation at boardroom level, where directors who are the pinnacle of the corporate safety culture provide leadership of the organisation.

Following the Cadbury Report, the Combined Code of the Committee on Corporate Governance was published in 1999 by the Institute of Chartered Accountants in England and Wales (ICAEW). It was applied to listed companies on the London Stock Exchange of which there are some 2,700 companies. The Code focuses on corporate governance which, whilst centered upon the financial aspects of an organisation, is linked to corporate losses in the wider context. That includes health and safety, a major risk factor for all organisations where there is a need for boardroom control.

The document is also known as the Turnbull Guidance, named after the chairman of the committee, Nigel Turnbull, and it provides a structure for assessing the effectiveness of a company's risk and control process which encompasses health and safety as a key factor in the management process.

The guidance identifies risk assessment as a board members' issue and determines that the company should have clear objectives to ensure that they have been communicated to employees so as to provide effective direction on the identification and assessment of risk. This should ensure that significant internal and external health and safety risks are identified and assessed, and that there is knowledge by management and others within the company as to what risks are acceptable to the board.

Control is a key factor within management and that requires the board to have clear strategies for dealing with the significant risks that have been identified. This is established within the company's culture, code of conduct, human resource, operating procedures and policies that support the overall business objectives including risk management. Senior management has to demonstrate, through its actions as well as its policies, the necessary commitment to ensure competence and integrity so as to develop a culture of trust within the company. The control element needs to ensure that responsibilities and accountability are clearly defined and that decisions are made and actions taken by the appropriate people and, in a diverse organisation, effectively co-ordinated.

Board members must communicate to their employees what is expected of them and define in detail the scope of their freedom to act and make decisions. This would include internal and outsourced activities regarding health and safety. The management must ensure that the people in the company, as well as its providers of outsourced services, have the competence to fulfil the company's objectives in supporting the management of the organisation's health and safety risks. Because risks within an organisation are subject to constant change, there needs to be controls in place that can reflect new or changing risks or operational deficiencies.

Information and communication are vital to any organisation and it is important that management and the board members receive timely, relevant and reliable reports on health and safety issues that could affect the business objectives. The sources should evolve from both inside and outside the organisation providing information that allows for decision-making and management review of health and safety.

There will also need to be periodic reporting procedures, including half-yearly and annual reporting where matters relating to health and safety are on the agenda. This should identify that there are effective communication channels that will allow individuals to report suspected breaches of laws, regulations or concerns in respect to health and safety.

To ensure compliance, there is a requirement to have systems structured within the organisation's overall business operations that are accessed by senior management to monitor the effectiveness of the policies, processes and activities related to health and safety. These processes are required to review the company's ability to re-evaluate risks and make suitable amendments as an effective response to changes. That in turn requires there to be a system to monitor any follow-up procedures in order to ensure that the appropriate changes or actions are carried out in response to changes identified through risk management.

The systems will allow the board or board committees to ensure the effectiveness of the ongoing processes of risk and control matters, which should include identifying any significant health and safety issues and the degree of risk. To complete the control process there needs to be specific arrangements for management to report to the board on health and safety risk and control matters.

The statement 'good governance is good business' is the foundation of corporate governance, encompassing the management of financial and operating risks within an organisation. An important ingredient within the organisation's operations is health and safety and, as such, must occupy an equal place within an organisation activity.

> **Help point:** This section has provided further evidence of the need for senior management to have proactive health and safety policies and procedures. It further emphasises the need for health and safety to be a senior management issue and not one to be delegated downwards in the organisation.

'Off the shelf' health and safety

4.4   Health and safety cannot be bought 'off the shelf': it is not a commodity that can be bought simply by entering a store and declaring that you want to buy some health and safety for your undertaking. It is possible to buy a computer package that purports to offer a safety system so that when all the appropriate boxes have been completed it produces a safety policy and a policy statement. The failing with that system is that every undertaking, no matter its size, is different. This means that the 'off the shelf' option does not fulfil the requirement if health and safety is a serious issue in your undertaking. In some cases, the differences may not be highly visible, for example, a number of shop premises in a shopping mall. However, the principal difference is the people – the human element. The human element is important because people die, are injured and suffer long illnesses through workplace incidents.

Those establishing a business will have to prepare a business plan, open a bank account and employ the services of an accountant. It is accepted that with new businesses there is generally a need to be able to borrow money and there are taxes to pay and venture into the world of VAT. The business will, depending upon its activities need plant, equipment and products etc, all of which will allow it to operate.

There will also be a requirement to insure the business with employers' liability and other appropriate insurance cover and this is the only time that health and safety will become apparent. In many cases, this will require completing a form and ticking a box that declares that the company has some basic health and safety documentation. People do not generally declare that they have any high-risk activities and so it is quickly passed over to get to the nub of how many employees and what type of activities are to be carried out. This will probably be the only time that the question of health and safety is raised, which, of course, is everybody else's concern – it does not apply to us.

> ➤   **Help point:** The law requires every new business employing more than five people to have a written health and safety policy. Yes, a blank copy can be obtained and filled in with brief details but there is no ownership of what is written and, generally, the contents bear no resemblance to the business. It could be argued that if health and safety is not adopted within the workplace then the health and safety of customers is not a consideration. Health and safety is a part of the businesses culture, both in the workplace and outside of it.

Health and safety is a matter of leadership, which is the theme of this book. The authors believe that if there is no leadership, then there is no positive safety culture. Negative management cannot buy leadership. Of course, the negative manager can provide training courses and get people to do the things that are required because they pay the wages. The negative manager can use threats with loss of job or no promotion. That may get the job done, but those at the receiving end have no respect for those who command and only go through the process because they have to. This negative, potentially threatening culture exists everywhere and can even penetrate undertakings that think everything is in good order.

Board members' ownership of health and safety

4.5 The adoption of a corporate governance structure for any sized organisation must be considered as being a valuable, if not vital, tool available to management. As part of an organisation's corporate health and safety management system, the HSC introduced the guidance 'Directors Responsibilities for Health and Safety' (INDG343) for board members of all types of organisations.

The objective is to ensure that risks to employees and those not employed are properly managed, and the focus is on company directors to establish effective management of health and safety risks with emphasis on the following key issues:

- maximise the well-being and productivity of all people working for an organisation;

- stop people getting injured, ill or killed through work activities;

- improve the organisation's reputation in the eyes of customers, competitors, suppliers, other stakeholders and the wider community;

- avoid damaging effects on turnover and profitability;

- encourage better relationships with contractors and more effective contracted activities;

- minimise the likelihood of prosecution and consequent penalties.

It is important to note that while the guidance uses the term 'director' to indicate a member of the board, the guidance applies to other undertakings that do not have to have a director to comply with the law. Therefore, the guidance must be deemed to apply to trust executives, trustees, partners, etc.

The guidance is not compulsory and undertakings are free to take other action, but if they follow the guidance they will generally be doing enough to comply with the law and, in the legal sense, the guidance can be used to illustrate good practice.

There are five action points which identify that:

- the board needs to accept formally and publicly its collective role in providing health and safety leadership for its organisation;

- the board needs to ensure that all of its decisions reflect its health and safety intentions, as described in the health and safety policy statement;

- the board needs to recognise its role in engaging the active participation of workers in providing health and safety;

- the board needs to ensure that it is kept informed of, and alert to, relevant health and safety risk management issues;

- the HSC recommends that boards appoint one of their number to be the health and safety director.

It is the last action that has evoked most comments and concerns as many directors and organisations see the appointed director as being the 'scapegoat' for the other directors or board members when things go wrong. There is no intention for there to be an individual exposed for the failings of the board, providing that the individual who has responsibility for health and safety has not been negligent. The role of the director appointed – and the HSC would ideally like to see the Chairman, Chief Executive or the head of an undertaking appointed to that role – is to ensure that there is in place an effective and positive system for health and safety.

➤ **Help point:** Ross Cranston QC MP has drafted and presented a Ten-Minute Rule Bill that would impose duties on directors. It proposes to take the HSC's 'Directors Responsibilities for Health and Safety' guidance forward into legislation. At the time of writing, this Bill has not made further progress.

Management through leadership

4.6   It will be seen that all levels of management must have leadership skills in order to operate their undertaking effectively with specific regard to health and safety. Many will argue that they are managers but few are leaders and that is the difference. Management has become a wide and diverse description of those who have some form of control or responsibility within an undertaking. However, the logical concept of management falls to directors and senior persons at senior management level. Middle management will fill the gap between the top and bottom of the undertaking and supervisory levels provide management of the workforce. Many have adopted the word 'management' in their job title and some managers control by power as opposed to leadership. All of the 'management' functions, with regard to health and safety, have equal interlinked responsibilities and the failure of any of those functions will severely weaken the structure.

There are a number of influences, both internal and external, that can affect an organisation's health and safety culture. In a highly competitive and changing commercial environment, the economy, public expectations, shareholders and viability are key influences. This can also include a poor accident record with resulting potential for disruptive production outputs. If an undertaking fails to trade effectively it becomes unviable and will cease to trade. Undertakings operate with corporate policies and mission statements which detail the high level of all encompassing objectives. Devised and adopted by senior management they are the driving force for their commitment to safety and the importance given to compliance. This clearly means that senior management's attitudes and behaviours have a direct impact on the workforce who will follow the example. If senior management does not care and does not encompass health and safety as part of the corporate culture, then they cannot expect the workforce to take the lead.

This 'no interest' attitude can transgress into other areas of the workplace activities and affect production and co-operation. It can also be the catalyst for increased incidents and that has a serious detrimental impact on the morale of the workforce. This attitude, where little regard to the well being of the staff is demonstrated, will result in a high staff turnover.

Management of health and safety risks

4.7   Every undertaking has different circumstances surrounding its exposure to hazard and risk. A large undertaking may expose its employees and those not employed to minimum risk, while a small undertaking may have a high hazard activity with the subsequent high-level risks. Therefore, all undertakings require safety management systems that are developed specifically to meet the undertakings needs, all based upon a number of basic principles. A key factor is the requirement for management to develop a system which it owns and shows commitment, but also of knowledge, and it is the knowledge of a particular industry and organisation that is important.

An article by Trevor Kletz in 'Safety and Health Practitioner', December 1996, identifies that a good example is for management to learn from the past, such as with the Aberfan disaster in 1966. The village in South Wales was the scene of a colliery tip slide that engulfed part of the village with the result that 144 people were killed, most of which were children. The underlying cause of the disaster was that the tip had been located over a stream on sloping ground. This is a classic management failure highlighted through an extract of the official report, which states:

'forty years before it occurred, we have the basic cause of the Aberfan disaster recognised and warned against. But, as we shall see, it was a warning which went largely unheeded ... Tip slides are not new phenomena. Although not frequent, they have happened throughout the world and particularly in South Wales for many years, and they have given rise to an extensive body of literature available long before the disaster ... In 1939 there was a tip slide at Cilfynydd in South Wales ... Its speed and destructive effect were comparable with the disaster at Aberfan, but fortunately no school, house or person lay in its path ... It could not fail to have alerted the minds of all reasonably prudent personnel employed in the industry of the dangers lurking in coal tips ... the lesson if ever learnt, was soon forgotten ... In 1944 another tip at Aberfan slid 500–600 feet. Apparently, no one troubled to investigate why it had slipped, but a completely adequate explanation was to hand ... it covered 400 feet of a totally unculverted stream ... Why was there this general neglect? Human nature being what it is, we think the answer to this question lies in the fact that ... there is no previous case of loss of life due to tip stability'.

In addition to the lack of management knowledge in respect to accidents both large and small involving employees and those not employed, there are cases where management do not accept responsibility for accidents and the issue is identified by Denis Smith in the *Safety and Health Practitioner*, February 1998, who states:

'Despite the presentation of data which shows that health and safety makes financial as well as moral sense, there are still clear barriers to making the necessary step change. The first is that managers show a clear reluctance to blame themselves for accidents, despite research that shows the importance of latent managerial error in accident generation. Why then would managers be willing to accept many of the non-intangible costs associated with accidents such as, opportunity costs, loss of reputation and the like? While they are more likely to acknowledge the more tangible costs of damage, compensation, loss of production, loss of product and raw materials, it is unlikely that they will accept that the management function has been instrumental in creating these costs - indeed, the search for scapegoats serves to legitimise management actions. Secondly, many organisations have shown clear reluctance to change their procedures and systems in the wake of accidents occurring elsewhere because they believe that it couldn't happen to them'.

The commentary continues to state:

'management plays a central role in the process of failure by providing the environmental and cultural conditions in which operator error occurs. Management, after all, is responsible for the development of standard operating procedures and is an important element in the development of a safety culture. It is also important to note that many managerial decisions have a long latency period before their implications are known, thus embedding an error cost within the system. Such strategic decisions can obviously play a major role in system safety'.

This is clearly a poignant statement although dated 1998, especially when reviewing a subject such as corporate killing, for it is management failure that will expose an organisation not only to accidents but also to charges under the proposed offence which is founded on management failure.

The health and safety professional

4.8　　A major concern for directors and those who are responsible at senior level is that, to ensure compliance with health and safety legislation, they need to determine the competence of their health and safety advisors, whether they are employed or contracted in as consultants. Good money, time and energy could be wasted if the service received leaves the company exposed when things go wrong.

The first step for the boardroom is to ensure that those engaged in health and safety are professionally competent and that can be achieved through the individual being recognised as a member of a professional body, such as the Institution of Occupational Safety and Health (IOSH). IOSH is the only health and safety body that currently operates a Registered Safety Practitioner scheme where the individuals have to submit evidence of competence, be interviewed for approval and have to maintain a Continuous Professional Development (CPD) portfolio. Other bodies such as the International Institute of Safety and Risk Management (IIRSM) and the Royal Society of the Prevention of Accidents provide valuable information to their members.

➢　**Help point:** The recognised status of a safety professional is as a Registered Safety Practitioner (RSP). IOSH is the lead professional body for health and safety in Europe and the professional status of any member can be checked by one quick phone call (IOSH membership telephone number: 0116 2573100). The IIRSM also requires it members to have accredited qualifications and confirmation of membership can be done through the organisation by telephoning 0208600 5538/5539.

Health and safety professionals cannot be complacent whether employed or self-employed. They have legal duties and failure on their part to meet those obligations can have serious implications. This means that safety professionals need to safeguard their activities and not be exposed, such as in the case of Charles Ian Hemrich who was found guilty under section 7 of the HSWA 1974 for failing to take reasonable care of himself and other persons. He was fined £3,000 with £3,000 costs.

Hemrich had been employed as a health and safety manager at Fatty Arbuckles head office. At the time of the case, the company had gone into receivership and so could be prosecuted. The case involved Mark Thorne, aged 17, who was employed by the company and died whilst 'deck scrubbing' the floor of the restaurant's kitchen after the premises had closed. The process required a lot of water lying on the floor in which he was standing. He came into contact with an incorrectly wired 1960s plate warmer which electrocuted him.

The case revealed that the company had been breaching health and safety legislation for several years before Hemrich was employed. Further, the duty to arrange risk assessments rests with the employer and not with an employee. However, Hemrich had focused on food hygiene and not health and safety compliance and had not brought any safety failings to the attention of the company's directors. It was accepted that while Hemrich did not directly or remotely cause the death of Thorne, the lack of risk assessments over a prolonged period made an incident more likely and he was the scapegoat for the failings of the company.

Hemrich's job as risk manager was not to act as legal adviser to the company, but to get risk management procedures in place. He was dealt with as not causing the death but contributing to it. There was no information as to his competence as a health and safety advisor and it is a matter that the courts must address when dealing with such cases. Many people only have the most basic health and safety qualifications and when things go wrong they are there to carry the can for management failures.

> ➢ **Help point:** The above case is a sharp reminder to both senior management and those with responsibility for health and safety to plan the work, communicate with senior management, and monitor activities. Clearly, the company had a negative safety culture and it resulted in a death and had a serious impact on the health and safety manager. The lesson is for the health and safety professional, whether an employee or a consultant, to advise senior management on a regular and formal basis all aspects of health and safety in the undertaking and, most importantly, to maintain a written record.

What are the benefits to be gained from having health and safety policies, systems and procedures? Senior management may see it as a 'pay out' situation, and what does the undertaking get in return? There is evidence to show that good health and safety is good for a business. It is good for an organisation's name, staff, customers/clients, insurance company and its profits. The cost of getting it right before it goes wrong is the cost effective option. Ask anybody who has been on the other side, for example, in court. How long has it taken to build the business and at what cost if the company is lost? Therefore, in order to meet the objectives of corporate governance, the health safety and welfare of everybody connected with a business, either employed or as a contractor or a member of the public, must be a key corporate policy.

Safety Management System HSG65

4.9   In order that directors and senior management, as well as those involved in health and safety management within a corporation, have information available to them, a practical guide 'Successful Health and Safety Management' (HSG65) has been produced by the HSE. The key elements of this guidance apply to any organisation, from multi-nationals to small enterprises, and comprise policy, organisation, planning, and measurement of performance, auditing and reviewing performance (see Figure 1 below).

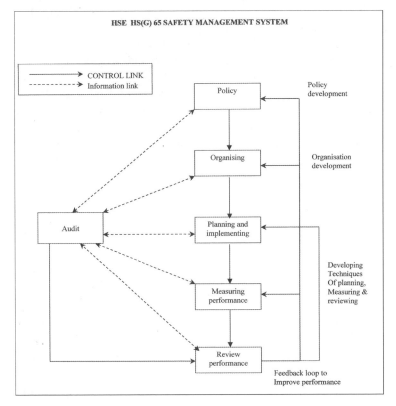

Figure 1

By adopting this system, the directors and management have to establish a corporate policy with regard to health and safety in order to ensure that all employees are motivated to be involved in the organisation's vision, values and beliefs. This means that senior management has to provide leadership in the development of a positive health and safety culture. Planning is an important part of an organisation's system as it is aimed at identifying hazards and minimising or removing risks. This has placed the onus on the management of an organisation that creates the risk, controls the risks and this is undertaken by risk assessments. The objective is to develop safe methods and procedures for working as part of a corporate health and safety culture.

The management, having undertaken the risk evaluation and mitigation process, needs to ensure that what has been adopted is effective. This is achieved by the measuring of performance, which will identify strengths and weaknesses within the system. By analysis of the information, management can maintain effective control of the corporation's activities in respect to safety and health.

Management can monitor progress of the corporate safety system, through feedback from all levels of the work force, either through union officials, safety representatives or other appointed spokespersons and, if necessary, individuals who raise specific concerns. While this can be effective in theory, what happens in practice may provide a different story and therefore the system needs to be audited, preferably by an independent source, who can identify positive and negative outcomes. There should be access to every level of the corporation's work force, including the chief executive or managing director, so that the safety management system is seen to be transparent within the organisation and part of its culture.

Chapter 5

Directors' Responsibilities and the Law

Introduction

5.0   A corporation's board is governed by a number of laws which place duties upon them. Among those laws is that of the health, safety and welfare of their employees as well as those who are not employed but are affected by the activities of the business. It can be argued that those at boardroom level or the equivalent in non-incorporated businesses have little knowledge or understanding of health and safety law. They will argue that it is a matter for insurance and their human resource or personnel departments and that their role is to make the business profitable and marketable.

It can be further argued that health and safety does not generally feature in management training and development programmes, but it is one of the most important dimensions to an effective, proactive and profitable business. The question now will be why? As with many things in life the answer is not straight forward, but it does affect key issues such as profit, insurance and prestige. The 'run of the mill' director or equivalent will not acknowledge this but the 'leader' will and this person will have adopted health, safety and welfare into the business as an integrated part of the corporate operation. The 'run of the mill' director will still not be sold on the concept and so it is necessary to focus on the legal obligations that are becoming more onerous for those who are not part of the leadership school of thought and action.

Management of health and safety

5.1   The Management of Health and Safety at Work Regulations 1992 (SI 1992/2051) was implemented as a result of the EC Directive 89/391/EEC 'on the introduction of measures to encourage improvements in the safety and health of workers at work'. The original Regulations have had to be amended several times since 1992 and because of the significant amendments, the Management of Health and Safety at Work Regulations

1999 (SI 1999/3242) (MHSWR) came into force which supersedes the previous Regulations as well as incorporating other legislation. The 1999 Regulations are published with an Approved Code of Practice (which has special legal status) and Guidance. The Regulations are based upon the requirements for every undertaking to identify and manage risks through the process of risk assessments of health and safety hazards present in the workplace that is not a new concept. Legislation governing the use of asbestos, hazardous substances and noise all imposed duties on the employer to assess the risks from specific workplace hazards and then identify and implement appropriate measures to reduce the risks.

The MHSWR extends that requirement to all employers (and the self-employed) and to all workplaces covered by the Health and Safety at Work etc Act 1974 (HSWA 1974) from the simplest office to workplaces with hazardous processes.

➢ **Help point:** Full guidance is available for the management of health and safety at work in the 'Management of Health and Safety at Work Regulations 1999 (SI 1999/3242), Approved Code of Practice and Guidance, L2, Her Majesty's Stationery Office, ISBN 0 7176 2488 9.

Identifying hazards

5.2   The first step is to recognise the hazards and risks that are found in a particular work environment, which leads the employer to identify hazards and ensure that arrangements are in place to mitigate against the risk. These arrangements should include the effective planning, organisation, control, monitoring and review of the preventive and protective measures.

There is a requirement for employers to undertake health surveillance, which means having regard to the risks to their health and safety that are identified by the assessment.

The employer has a duty to have health and safety assistance by appointing one or more competent persons to assist him in undertaking compliance measures. That person shall be regarded as competent where he has sufficient training and experience or knowledge and other qualities to enable him properly to assist.

It is also a duty for the employer to provide procedures to manage serious and imminent danger and for danger areas that are hazardous for employees. These can include a written emergency action plan and a procedure for identifying foreseeable events that need to be covered. Employers have to provide information to an employee that is relevant, understandable and achievable for:

(a)   any risks to their health and safety identified by the assessment; and

(b)   the preventive and protective control measures.

Human error

5.3   Estimates attribute up to 80% of accidents to human factors with human error being an element in many major incidents. In the past, many accidents were attributed to human error but the root cause of accidents evolves through management failure to train and have effective systems of work. Placing blame for incidents on human error was seen as a viable explanation and beyond the control of an undertakings management. This is not acceptable and the human element needs to be managed in the same way and with the same seriousness as technical and systems failures.

The management of health and safety must review the types and causes of human failures and develop ways of reducing them. Management needs to develop better design of tasks, equipment and procedures, and train their staff. Critical issues for many undertakings are operational issues that include:

• shift work and the potential implications;

• communications with shift workers;

• employees' perception of risk;

• employees' behaviour; and

• the need for a positive safety culture.

Management will need to examine:

• **the job** – which encompasses what people are being asked to do, such as workload, task, environment, controls and procedures;

• **the individual** – the person doing the job, their competence, skills, personality and attitudes;

• **the organisation** – the health and safety resources, the corporate culture, works systems and communications.

The principal elements

5.4   All undertakings will have three principal elements that encompass the management of health and safety:

(a)   people;

(b)   systems of work; and

(c)   plant and equipment.

All of these elements must interface and be considered in the management process. A failure in any one of the elements could be the cause of an accident. The three elements flow into the undertaking, which extends its management of health and safety to a range of *customers.*

The people element includes a diverse range of individuals who may be direct employees, members of the public, contractors, subcontractors, self-employed, homeworkers. All of these individuals have to interface into the undertaking and must be competent to undertake the tasks they are assigned.

The systems of work element include issues such as management of risks, operational procedures, emergency planning and management control and supervision.

The hardware element includes all plant, machinery, equipment 'and vehicles. These are the elements of an undertaking that will need to extend its management system of health and safety to its clients, customers as well as those who are contracted into the organisation to carry out work.

Safe system of work

5.5   The term 'safe system of work' is broad based and includes the precautions that must be made to account for the safety of the workers at all times. This includes having sufficient persons to do the job, and that those persons are competent to undertake the work tasks. In addition, it extends to those not employed who have to be safeguarded against harm caused by the activities of the undertaking.

The definition of a 'safe system of work' is most effectively dealt with by the examination of cases that have progressed through the appeals system. While it is not definitive, it does provide the details of what the management failed to do, the actions of the employee, and the legal determination.

A leading case for safe systems of work is *General Cleaning Contractors Ltd v Christmas [1953] AC 180, [1952] 2 All ER 110*. This is the case of a window cleaner, employed by General Cleaning Contractors Ltd, who was cleaning the outside of the windows of a club. There were no fittings to which he could attach a safety belt so he stood on the sill of the window, a method commonly used by his colleges. A defective sash window fell on his hand, causing him to let go and fall. He was awarded damages against both the employer and the occupier of the premises.

However, the decision against the occupier was reversed on appeal because the defective window was not an 'unusual danger' of which the occupier was bound to warn the window cleaner.

The employer appealed to the House of Lords. The House of Lords ruled that where the practice of ignoring an obvious danger had developed, it was not reasonable to expect the individual employee to take the initiative in devising a system of work against the danger. This is regardless of the fact that other systems of work were not practical. General Cleaning Contractors Ltd were still obliged to consider the situation, to take reasonable steps to provide a system that would be reasonably safe having regard to the dangers inherent in the operation and to ensure that its employees were instructed on how to prevent accidents in their work, including providing the implements. The employer had not done so and had not discharged its duty to the employee and, therefore, the appeal was dismissed.

This is a case that explains the relationship between the duty of care owed by employers and the obligations on workmen to take reasonable care for their own safety. Those at work are not in the position of employers when taking decisions and it was stated that:

> 'workmen do not perform their duties in the calm of the boardroom with the advice of experts. They have to make their decisions on narrow windowsills and other places of danger and in circumstances where the dangers are obscured by repetition'.

It is the responsibility of the employer to take the initiative in devising and using precautions and the workman is not expected to do so himself. If a man is doing work as specified and expected by his employer, and there has been a failure to take adequate precautions, then the blame should not rest on the man.

The main issue is whether the employer has taken responsibility with reasonable care to provide a safe system of work for the employees. Where a practice of ignoring an obvious danger has developed then it is not the workman's responsibility to devise a system to overcome it. When making a decision as to what is reasonable, the employer must take into account the conduct and long established practices in the trade.

Key issues

5.6   Lord Oaksey highlighted the key issues in the *General Cleaning Contractors* case:

> 'It is the duty of an employer to give such general safety instructions as a reasonably careful employer who has considered the problem presented by the work would give his workmen'.

Lord Oaksey continued to state:

> 'It is well known to employers ... that their workpeople are very frequently, if not habitually, careless about risks which their work may involve. It is ... for that very reason that the common law demands that employers should take reasonable care to lay down a reasonably safe system of work. Employers are not exempted from this duty by the fact that their men are experienced and might, if they were in the position of an employer, be able to lay down a reasonably safe system of work themselves. Workmen are not in a position of employers. Their duties are not performed in the calm atmosphere of a boardroom with the advice of experts. They have to make their decisions on narrow sills and other places of danger and in circumstances where dangers are obscured by repetition'.

Lord Reid said in the same case:

> 'Where the practice of ignoring an obvious danger has grown up I do not think that it is reasonable to expect an individual workman to take the initiative in devising and using precautions. It is the duty of the employer to consider the situation, to devise a suitable system, to instruct his men what they must do and to supply any implements that may be required'.

The general consensus of the legal ruling and commentators regards the definition of what is a safe system of work as being broad and open to interpretation. It is, therefore, a matter of fact and will be a matter for the courts to determine. It does, however, place the duty for the development of a safe system of work with the employer. It further places the duty on the employer to inform the employees of what is required.

Management of risk

5.7   Every undertaking has different circumstances surrounding its hazardous activities that could expose employees to a hazard where, in fact, they should not be undertaking hazardous activities. A large undertaking may expose its employees and those not employed to minimum risk, while a small undertaking may have a high hazard activity with the subsequent high-level risks. Therefore, all undertakings require safety management systems that are developed specifically to meet the undertakings needs, all based upon a number of basic principles.

> ➢ **Help point:** Senior management can delegate specific tasks to employees such as appointing a health and safety professional. That person must be competent and have direct access to senior management to provide professional advice to the board. Senior management cannot delegate its responsibilities and, if there are failures, then those on the board are accountable.

Risk assessment

5.8 The Management of Health and Safety at Work (Amendment) Regulations 1994 (SI 1994/2865), reg: 3 states:

'Risk Assessment—

(1) Every employer shall make a suitable and sufficient assessment of:

(a) the risks to the health and safety of his employees to which they are exposed whilst they are at work; and

(b) the risks to the health and safety of persons not in his employment arising out of or in connection with the conduct by him of his undertaking ...'

Because of the importance of risk assessment in undertakings, the Health and Safety Executive (HSE) produced a guidance, '5 Steps to Risk Assessment', which contains information on good practices which, while not compulsory, are of help to management in understanding what is required and how to set about undertaking risk assessments.

➤ **Help point:** '5 Steps to Risk Assessment' INDG163 (HSE) – The leaflet contains a blank risk assessment form that can be adopted by most businesses and industries, focusing on topics of hazards, who might be harmed, whether the risk is adequately controlled and what further action is necessary to control the risks. The success of the guidance gave rise to an updated version to be produced in 1999 with the same title which retains the same message, setting the basis for employers and self-employed to assess the risks in the workplace with the aim of ensuring that there are sufficient precautions taken to make sure that no-one gets hurt. It explains that accidents and ill health can affect a business, through lost output, machinery damage, increased insurance costs or court action. (The latest reprint, July 2003, can be found at www.hse.gov.uk/pubns/indg163.pdf)

The MHSWR states that there is a legal requirement to assess risks in the workplace. The fact that risk assessment is enshrined in law means that risks have to be assessed and controlled. Failures that cause deaths at work could show a management failure to heed advise and adopt safe practices.

➤ **Help point:** The Regulations state that risks have to be identified and then managed with the significant findings to be recorded. The authors advocate that all risk assessments are put in writing and it provides management with evidence that assessments have been carried out.

Organisational management

5.9   Organisations differ in size, location, type and management structure, and they will involve a range of hazards from very low to very high, providing a wide range of risks that have to be managed. It follows that the law pertaining to health and safety can also be complex and may not be readily understood by management, they may consider that their role is much wider than health and safety law. Senior management of many undertakings will argue that it is not financially viable to employ a competent health and safety professional.

Employers have to identify the capabilities and competencies of its staff and provide training where necessary, with the emphasis on health and safety. This can be achieved by providing adequate health and safety training when staff are recruited and when they are exposed to new or increased risks.

Employees also have duties when at work and that means that every employee has to use any machinery or equipment in accordance with the methods identified in the operating instructions and the training provided in the use of the equipment. The employee is required to inform his employer or any other employee if there is any work situation where it is considered that there could be a serious and immediate danger to a person's health and safety. Having done all of this, the employer has to investigate the situation and act appropriately, as it is the employer who has the ultimate responsibility for health and safety in the undertaking.

Employees should always have the right to stop work if it is unsafe and a survey of an undertaking's employees will provide an understanding of their feelings if they believe they have the right to stop work.

Senior management at board level, or its equivalent in an undertaking, will need to focus on its responsibilities. This clearly places the ownership of health and safety at the highest level of management in every organisation. It is, therefore, imperative that health and safety is adopted as an integral part of day-to-day activities and culture. Management will need show that they take suitable and sufficient steps to manage health and safety in the same way that they manage other aspects of the business. This is the situation no matter the size of an undertaking and it is a matter for those who create the risks to manage the risks.

While having management systems in place is no guarantee that criminal sanctions will not be imposed, a court will take into consideration the level of positive health and safety management.

Trevor Kletz identifies, in an article in 'The Safety and Health Practitioner', December 1996, that, overall, accident statistics show that smaller organisations have higher accident rates than larger organisations, but it is not known if the reason is that smaller organisations do not have the resources to adopt health and safety as a key business issue, or whether being a contractor implies that safety is a matter for the client and not them.

A client that has a comprehensive and effective health and safety management system can impart much of that knowledge and culture to those contracted in whatever form. In every situation a client must ensure that all contractors are protected from risks whilst working on its premises or site under its control. Equally, the contractors must not take any form of action that could place the client's employees at risk, which means that both clients and contractors have duties of care to each other as well as the public. He makes very valuable points about corporate memory as follows.

'The following actions can help us remember the lessons of the past. If we have paid the high price of an accident we should at least turn it into a learning experience.

- Include in every instruction, code and standard, a note on the reason it was introduced and accounts of accidents which would not have occurred if it had been followed.

- Describe old accidents as well as recent ones in safety bulletins and newsletters and discuss them at safety meetings: *giving the message once is not enough.*

- Follow up at regular intervals to see that the recommendations made after accidents are being followed, in design as well as operation.

- Remember that the first step down the road to the next accident occurs when someone turns a blind eye.

- Never remove equipment before you know why it was installed. Never abandon a procedure before you know why it was adopted.

- Include important accidents of the past in the training of undergraduates and company employees.

- Before experienced people retire, get them to write down their know-how, especially the information that younger and less experienced people are not aware of.

- Devise better retrieval systems so that we can find, more easily than at present, details of past accidents, in your own and other companies, and recommendations made afterwards.

The more diffuse the company structure, the more it devolves power to semi-autonomous managers, the easier it will be to avoid liability. This is of particular importance given the increasing tendency of many organisations specifically to decentralise safety services. It is clearly in the interest of shrewd and unscrupulous management to do so. If corporations perceive themselves to be at risk of prosecution, an analogous process of decentralisation within the corporation might be developed to evade liability.'

Secondly, the limits of criminal liability constructed by the identification doctrine do not reflect properly the limits of the moral responsibility of the corporation itself. This cannot be limited to responsibility for the acts of high-ranking officials such as company directors.

Priorities in hierarchical organisations like corporations are set predominantly from above. It is these priorities that determine the social context within which a corporation's shop floor workers and the like made decisions about working practices. A climate of safety or lack of safety may permeate the entire organisation; the climate is created at the highest level. Thus, if criminal law is to reflect this moral responsibility, in appropriate cases, legal responsibility ought to extend to acts done by the *hands* of corporation.

There are a number of key issues that apply to all undertakings and are imperative for the culture of any undertaking to eliminate if possible, any harm to any person. They are as follows:

- health and safety must be adopted as part of the undertakings business plan;

- leadership is the key, and that must come from the board members;

- systems that are compatible and understandable must be adopted;

- everybody in the undertaking must know and understand the health and safety standards senior management require;

- senior management must communicate with those in the undertaking to obtain feedback;

- contractors, part-time and agency staff must be integrated into the system;

- ownership of safety, health and environment includes everybody from top to bottom of the undertaking.

Duties of directors and employees

5.10 There already exists within the Health and Safety at Work etc Act 1974 (HSAWA 1974) offences for individuals including directors, managers, employees and others. Under the Act, a 'section 36 offence' is where there is the fault of another person, while section 37 is a corporate offence for directors, company secretaries and mangers. Section 7 is used for individuals. These three offences include a wide and diverse range of people who owe a duty of care to others with sanctions available when they fail in that duty.

HSWA 1974, s 37

5.11   The HSE and local authority enforcement officers can prosecute directors and senior company officers under section 37 of the HSWA 1974:

> 'Section 37 Offences by Bodies Corporate:
>
> Where an offence under any of the relevant statutory provisions (a) committed by a body corporate is proved to have been committed with the consent or connivance (b) of, or to have been attributable to any neglect on the part of, any director, manager, secretary or other similar officer (c) of the body corporate or a person who was purporting to act in any such capacity, he as well as the body corporate shall be guilty of that offence and shall be liable to be proceeded against and punished accordingly'.

It must first be established that the company committed an offence by breaching a duty imposed by the 1974 Act itself. It will then be necessary to show that the director 'consented' or 'connived' in the offence committed by the company, or that the corporate offence resulted from 'any neglect' on his or her part.

It has to be established that a director consents to the commission of an offence when he or she is 'well aware of what is going on and agrees to it'. It will be necessary to show that this agreement involved some positive action, which could be verbal, in writing or a gesture. It is important to note that the latter may offer difficulty in establishing proof to a level that would secure a conviction.

It can be considered that a director 'connives' in an offence when he is well aware of what is going on and whilst not actively encouraging what happens, allows it to continue and does nothing to stop the activity. As far as gathering evidence is concerned it should be easier to prove 'connivance' in that it has to be shown that the director was aware of the 'offence' and did nothing to stop it.

There is a need to prove 'neglect' on the part of a company officer who has a 'duty' to do whatever it is alleged he failed to do. However, the absence of *legal* duties does not preclude action as there is interpretation that shows neglect can also refer to the breach of *non-legal* duties.

HSWA 1974, s 7

5.12   Employees can be prosecuted under section 7 of the HSWA 1974 as they have a duty to take reasonable care for the health and safety of themselves and others who may be affected by their acts or omissions at work:

'Section 7 General Duties of Employees at Work:

To take reasonable care for the health and safety of himself and of other persons who may be affected by his acts or omissions at work ... any duty or requirement imposed upon his employer or any other person by or under any of the relevant statutory provisions, to co-operate with him so far as is necessary to enable that duty or requirement to be performed or complied with'.

This offence provides for the prosecution of an employee who knowingly undertakes an unsafe action where another is harmed as an outcome. An employee who, through an act of horseplay or skylarking while at work, causes another to be injured, that employee could be prosecuted. Any employee who provided with safety equipment refuses to wear or use the equipment or abide by safety procedures could be liable for prosecution.

In addition to the HSWA 1974, the Management of Health and Safety at Work Regulations 1999 impose additional duties on employees to report dangerous situations or shortcomings to the employer in matters of health and safety. It is often seen that the corporate body is prosecuted as having the ultimate general duty of care, with HSWA 1974, s 7 charges against an individual for specific acts or omissions.

A case profile shows that between 1996/97 and 2001/02 there were 87 'section 7' prosecutions commenced. The outcome resulted in individuals being convicted in 76 successful prosecutions. The total fines for all cases amounted to £5,375. The initial date was selected as being readily available to provide data. It is deemed sufficient to provide an overview of the number of cases taken under the section.

It is important to note that the fines for section 7 offences are minimal with an average fine of £895.00. A reason for this is that, generally, the individual will have lost his or her job and not be in receipt of an income. With a criminal record for a health and safety offence it will reduce the employability of the individual. Therefore, when the court assesses the financial status of those convicted it will generally be minimal and the fine is commensurate with available finances.

HSWA 1974, s 37

5.14 There are three individual offences under the HSWA 1974 that can be laid against individuals. They are not regularly used because, in particular with section 37, it is difficult to prove the offence. However, there is an increasing number of successfully prosecuted cases and it is relevant to provide details of example cases.

Section 37 case law

5.15   The following cases provide a background of the offences and the focus of individual liability showing the package of offence and the penalties that resulted in a successful prosecution under HSWA 1974, s 37.

Fresha Bakeries

5.16   'Leicester Bakers Ordered to Pay £628,000 after Double Deaths in Oven', stated the headlines of a HSE Press release. In the case of Harvestime Ltd, Fresha Bakeries, two directors and a manager were fined a total of £373,000 plus costs of £255,000 as a result of the death of two employees at their factory in Leicester on 16 May 1998. The two men had been sent into a giant oven to retrieve a broken part, using a slow moving conveyor belt to enter the oven where the temperature was more than 100 degrees and died as a result.

Fresha Bakeries were prosecuted under section 2 of the HSWA 1974 because they failed to provide a safe system of work. Harvestime were prosecuted under the same offence. Both companies were prosecuted under section 3 of the Act for failing to ensure persons not in their employ were exposed to danger. For these offences the companies were fined a total of £350,000.

Dennis Masters, the Chief Engineer and employee of Fresha Bakeries, was prosecuted under section 7 and fined £2,000. Brian Jones, an employee, was also prosecuted under section 7 and fined £1,000.

John Bridson, Managing Director of Harvestime Ltd, was prosecuted under section 37 of the HSWA 1974 and fined £10,000. He was also the Managing Director of Fresha Bakeries Ltd and was prosecuted under section 37 and fined £10,000. In total, John Bridston was fined £20,000. The costs were divided into £250,000 awarded against the companies and £5,000 against John Bridson.

The Post Office

5.17   The Post Office case provides a good example of a director being prosecuted but with no evidence offered. The incident was not fatal, and the penalty was minimal in the event of serious injuries.

On Friday 13 July 2001, the Post Office Royal Mail appeared in Birmingham Magistrates' Court being prosecuted by the HSE under section 3 of the HSAW 1974 for failing to ensure, so far as was reasonably practicable, that persons not in their employment were not exposed to risks to their safety. The managing Director of Post Office Property Holdings, Crenville Collins, also appeared, having been charged with section 37 of the Act in that, allegedly, an offence by a corporate body was committed with his consent or connivance or was attributable to any neglect on his part. The prosecution was as a result of an incident where a roofing contractor fell through a fragile roof light at the Post Office Road Transport Workshop in Birmingham, suffering serious injuries. The Post Office was fined £2,500. No evidence was offered on the charge against Mr Collins.

JM Enterprises of Wetherby Ltd

5.18   The case of JM Enterprises of Wetherby is an important case as it involves the prosecution of individuals on a number of offences and established a precedent for the enforcing authorities.

The directors, Nigel Jackson and John Mather of JM Enterprises (JME) of Wetherby Ltd, a firework manufacturer, were fined for health and safety breaches. Firework display organiser, Mick Mason, died in a massive explosion after he took four boxes of condemned Turbo 3 Rocket fireworks from the company to burn in his kiln. Mason lit a furnace, resulting in a massive explosion which killed him and due to the power of the explosion the upper kiln door was displaced 85 metres by the blast.

The rockets had been declared unsafe by trading standards officers. They contained barium nitrate, sulphur and aluminium powder, which is referred to as 'Flash composition', which means that it is a high-energy, rapidly burning composition that can explode violently. A company employee who had no formal training had, because of a lack of knowledge, passed the broken up, volatile fireworks to Mason. The fireworks were so unstable they could have exploded while being transported.

A parallel investigation identified that JME was an importer and supplier of fireworks, which involved large-scale importation of unclassified fireworks, which is illegal. Investigations showed that of 22 shipments, some 43% of fireworks imported in these consignments were unclassified. The HSE placed prohibition notices on the company to prevent transportation and supply of unclassified fireworks. The directors and a manager acting on behalf of the company breached the notices. Mather had, prior to the notices being issued, supplied fireworks to a wholesaler. Because the directors and managers had close control over the activities of the company, the individuals were prosecuted.

There were two serious charges:

1.   The directors (Jackson and Mather) pleaded guilty to a breach of a prohibition notice through consent or contrivance when they supplied unclassified fireworks to a wholesaler.

2.   Jackson and Mather admitted breach of a prohibition notice through their neglect in that they transported an unclassified X-O-Set to Newcastle airport. Mather had intended to take the firework on board

a plane to Poland. They both claimed to believe that the rocket was a dummy and contained no explosives. The rocket, which was in fact 'live', was discovered by security at Newcastle airport.

It is the first time that individual directors have been convicted for section 37 offences without the company being convicted of the same offence. The company, which was in receivership, and three individuals pleaded guilty to 24 offences. It is important to note that the HSE did not seek an order to disqualify either Mather or Jackson from acting as directors and both men are still employed in the firework industry in the UK. This case was important and the precedent is quoted:

> 'The HSE prosecuted the directors and manager under the section 37 of the Health and Safety at Work etc Act 1974 because of the close control that they exercised over the company ... Until the JME case, the interpretation of section 37(1) has always been that to secure a section 37(1) conviction of a director, the company has first to be convicted of a parallel offence. But this case also saw the HSE secure four convictions of one director and two of the other four offences for which the company had not been convicted. This has not happened before'.

A very important aspect of the case was the breach of a notice, which as opposed to the section 37 offence, caries the possibility of imprisonment.

> 'The directors appear fortunate to have avoided imprisonment and disqualification. Mather and Jackson were convicted respectively of four and three breaches of prohibition notices; such offence is one the few under the Health and Safety at Work etc Act 1974 that can result in imprisonment, accounting for three of the five prison sentences issued under the Act. One of the charges said that the notice had been contravened with the consent or connivance of Mr Jackson and Mr Mather. (All the other charges cited neglect.) The judge said he had considered a custodial sentence, but he felt that the offence that had involved consent or connivance – as opposed to the less serious neglect – concerned a risk that was insufficiently severe to merit prison.'

The case was successful to the degree that it set new guidelines for future cases. The downside must be the failure to obtain a custodial sentence, as it diminishes the weight and seriousness of a notice. The authorities use prohibition notices to stop an act that could result in serious injury or death. There is a right of appeal, which in this case did not appear to be an option taken. Therefore, the breach was a serious and calculated act but as the directors were not disqualified it weakened the success of the case.

Conclusion

5.19　This chapter has reviewed the implications for a director, executive senior partner, trustee or senior manager with regard to health and safety management failure. It has also looked at the implications for individuals.

Adopting health and safety within an undertaking and maintaining the momentum is a critical element of the duties imposed upon them. A company can lose an order and even lose money and survive, but to be indicted with blood on the hands is a whole new 'ball game' with potentially serious consequences. The law is to be strengthened against those who fail to lead and maintain a strong health and safety culture.

Chapter 6

Legal Considerations

Introduction

6.0   It is important for management to have an overview of the official bodies who can have an affect on their business. Inspectors form the Health and Safety Executive (HSE) and local government have a range of powers to undertake inspections with regard to health and safety matters and are appointed to undertake the duties. They can issue official notices, where the conditions have to be complied with (unless an appeal is made). They have the power to take into possession documents, equipment or substances it they are part of an investigation. They can take statements, both voluntary and tape recorded where a caution of possible prosecution is given. They can instigate a prosecution and even conduct the proceedings in a Magistrates' Court.

When there is a fatal accident the police will attend the scene and they will work with the health and safety inspector, to determine the implications for potential gross negligence on the part of an individual. The police have different powers and, unlike the health and safety inspector, they have powers of arrest. When the two are combined, their powers are considerable and for those being investigated it is paramount that they co-operate fully. This chapter will review the legal considerations that all concerned will be involved with and while the information is not exhaustive it provides a flavour of what faces every senior manager, manager, supervisor and, indeed, every employee.

Appointment and powers of inspectors

6.1   The authority for both the HSE and relevant local authorities to appoint inspectors and the very extensive powers which appointed inspectors have to enable them to inspect workplaces and take necessary measures with a view to enforcing relevant statutory provisions are set out in the Health and Safety at Work etc Act 1974, ss 19 and 20. Every enforcing authority can, under section 19 of the Act, appoint inspectors having determined that such persons have suitable qualifications it thinks are necessary to carry out the relevant statutory activities within its field of responsibility, and can terminate any appointment made under this section. The powers that the inspectors who have been appointed are the subject of section 20 of the Health and Safety at Work etc Act 1974 (HSWA 1974), and can exercise the following actions:

(1) Subject to the provisions of section 19 and this section, an inspector may, for the purposes of carrying into effect any of the relevant statutory provisions within the field of responsibility of the enforcing authority which appointed him, exercise the powers set out in subsection (2) below.

(2) The powers of an inspector referred to in the preceding subsection are the following, namely:

(a) at any reasonable time (or, in a situation which in his opinion is, or may be, dangerous at any time) to enter any premises which he has reason to believe it is necessary for him to enter;

(b) to take with him a constable if he has reasonable cause to apprehend any serious obstruction in the execution of his duty;

(c) without prejudice to the preceding paragraph on entering any premises by virtue of (a) above to take with him:

(i) any other person duly authorised by his (the inspector's) enforcing authority; and

(ii) any equipment or materials required for any purpose for which the power of entry is being exercised;

(d) to make such examination and investigation as may in any circumstances be necessary;

(e) as regards any premises which he has power to enter, to direct that those premises or any part of them, or anything therein, shall be left undisturbed (whether generally or in particular respects) for so long as is reasonably necessary for the purpose of any examination or investigation under (d) above;

(f) to take such actions and photographs and make such recordings as he considers necessary for the purpose of any examination or investigation under (d) above;

(g) to take samples of any articles or substances found in any premises which he has power to enter, and of the atmosphere in, or in the vicinity of, any such premises;

(h)   in the case of any article or substance found in any premises which he has power to enter, being an article or substance which appears to him to have caused or to be likely to cause danger to health or safety, to cause it to be dismantled or subjected to any process or test (but not so as to damage or destroy it unless this is in the circumstances necessary for the purpose mentioned in subsection (1) above);

(i)   in the case of such article or substance as is mentioned in the preceding paragraph to take possession of it and detain it for so long as is necessary for all or any of the following purposes, namely:

    (i)   to examine it and do to it anything which he has power to do under that paragraph;

    (ii)   to ensure that it is not tampered with before his examination of it is completed;

    (iii)   to ensure that it is available for use as evidence in any proceedings for an offence under any of the relevant statutory provisions or any proceedings relating to a notice under sections 21 or 22;

(j)   to require any person whom he has reasonable cause to believe to be able to give any information relevant to any examination or investigation under (d) above to answer (in the absence of persons other than a person nominated by him to be present and any persons whom the inspector may allow to be present) such questions as the inspector thinks fit to ask and to sign a declaration of the truth of his answers;

(k)   to require the production of, inspect, and take copies of or of any entry in:

    (i)   any books or documents which by virtue of any of the relevant statutory provisions are required to be kept; and

    (ii)   any other books or documents which it is necessary for him to see for the purposes of any examination or investigation under (d) above;

(l)   to require any person to afford him such facilities and assistance with respect to any matters or things within that person's control or in relation to which that person has responsibilities as are necessary to enable the inspector to exercise any of the powers conferred on him by this section;

(m)   any other power which is necessary for the purpose mentioned in subsection (1) above.

The police have separate powers and, in the case of deaths at work, that involves working for the Coroner by undertaking an investigation into the circumstances surrounding the death. They then make a report to the Coroner who will use the information for the inquest. If there is evidence of negligence, the police will work with the inspectors to submit to the Crown Prosecution Service (CPS) for consideration for manslaughter. Numerous cases are submitted in this way but few are proceeded with as there is a very strict and high evidential test and it has to be in public interest. In addition, it is expensive to prosecute a manslaughter case and, therefore, there has to be a realistic prospect of conviction.

Prospect of prosecution

6.2   Having reviewed the powers of inspectors and having the knowledge that where there is a fatal incident the police will be involved, the question that will be on the mind of all senior managers is what are the prospects of a prosecution following a workplace accident or a breach of health and safety legislation? For the authorities, prosecution is the ultimate sanction available in respect to health and safety where the alleged breach of a general duty requires the prosecution only to prove a failure to ensure safety. The defence may prove that they could not have been expected to know of the risk and it was therefore not reasonably practicable to do more. In such circumstances, neither the HSE, or local government would wish to prosecute if there were real prospects of the defendant showing that he could not reasonably have known about the risks. They will, as part of the investigation process, seek information about the defendant's knowledge, such as the collective knowledge within the company.

The knowledge within the company may be identified from information provided by suppliers, its customers, and from communications inside the company. In addition, inspectors may have previously dealt with a company in a way which proves actual knowledge. Documents may include board minutes, the company's safety policy statements, the contracts which the companies have made, training records, maintenance records, and information provided with machines, equipment and substances used by the company.

➢   **Help point:** It is imperative that the activities of the undertaking, no matter its size, are recorded and filed. When faced with an investigation it will be vital and credible evidence to prove compliance with the law. It may be that such information is not sufficient, but it will mitigate the failure of compliance. Further, records and documents should be readily available for inspection as it shows that maintaining records is an integral part of day-to-day business and not something that sits on a shelf gathering dust.

A review of the documentation and records will be made by an expert who will need to consider all such information and bring before the court other information which shows the standards normally to be expected, often by reference to publications including practitioner's books, British Standards, and industry standards. Assistance may be obtained from documents the company has published, such as advertising literature. Companies House will provide information that will give an indication of the size and management of a registered incorporated body, including its profits. However, information about an unincorporated body, such as the self-employed or partnerships, may be less readily available and so it is important to have some form of records available.

For the authorities to obtain a conviction for a health and safety offence it is often sufficient to rely on the event, which caused the incident, combined with the companies own documents and an expert opinion that it was reasonably practicable to do more.

Investigating deaths at work

6.3   The most serious situation for any undertaking is when a workplace death occurs. That can involve an employee, a contractor on site or a member of the public. The HSE investigates deaths at work within its field of responsibility with a need to establish the cause of death, identify and deal with any safety issues, and address any questions of blame. A police detective of supervisory rank should attend the scene to join a safety inspector to commence the investigation. In the meantime, the scene should be left undisturbed, as there are a number of offences that might otherwise be committed. The employer should commence an immediate investigation to determine the cause and take remedial actions to eliminate further harm.

As already discussed, the HSE inspector has extensive powers to investigate for the purposes of ensuring health and safety and gathering evidence in relation to a potential prosecution. If it appears that there is evidence that the person died as a result of gross negligence, that matter may be investigated more extensively by the police and HSE inspectors, the police taking the lead in the investigation. If activities at the site give rise to a risk of serious personal injury the inspector will serve a notice prohibiting such activities. If there is a breach of any health and safety legislation the inspector may serve a notice requiring improvements. Any immediate lessons concerning safety will be communicated to the employer and the employees or their union representative.

The Coroner's Officer may also gather information, which is required in order to conduct the Inquest. If there is a major incident, the Health and Safety Commission (HSC) can set up a public Inquiry and examples are the Southall Inquiry and Lord Cullen's Inquiry into the Ladbroke Grove rail crash. Such inquiries consider longer-term issues. Prosecutions for manslaughter following a work-related death are comparatively rare but prosecutions under safety legislation frequently follow deaths at work. The HSE estimates that approximately 70% of industrial accidents are avoidable. The number of reportable accidents within HSE is approximately 20% of the accident rate for its sector. Whilst the HSE assist the police in any manslaughter investigation following a death arising from work, it has no role in relation to any CPS prosecution, although it may provide expert evidence. If there are also offences on the indictment relating to health and safety, the HSE will continue to assist in relation to the prosecution generally but the CPS will take the lead.

As already stated, a death at work will initially involve the police, (possibly especially appointed Coroner's Officers) and HSE inspectors and that has in the past caused some conflicts of interest. An inspector was very much aware of that when in the early hours of 31 July 1995 he received a telephone call to advise that a diver working in the southern sector of the North Sea gas fields had been killed. He had been dragged into the moving propellers of the diving support vessel from which he was working. Two specialist diving inspectors began the investigation process and that required, in the first instance, a helicopter flight to the vessel. Others involved in that initial investigation included a Detective Sergeant, four Detective Constables, a scene of crime officer (SOCO) and two Coroner's Officers.

Aboard the vessel, each group followed its own procedures and investigated for different purposes, the police sought to identify any 'foul play', the HSE Inspectors looked for the cause and reasons for the accident and to take action to stop a re-occurrence and the Coroner's Officers considered a combination of both. Co-operation between the groups was at this point cordial because each group had different objectives. There were items of evidence discarded by the police as irrelevant, but which were vital to the HSE investigation and were therefore taken into possession by the inspectors. Statements were taken, some jointly, others independently and although the police statements varied to some degree from those of the HSE, all were vital in that initial investigation.

What had occurred involved a diver working from a diving bell in about 25 metres of water whose umbilical had become fouled in the moving propellers of the vessel resulting in the death of the diver. The Diving Support Vessel (DSV) remains on station through a system called Dynamic

Positioning (DP) where computers control the speed and direction of the vessel's propellers, to keep it on a pre-determined location. Because the propellers are rotating' it is vital to keep the diver and his umbilical clear of them. The diver's umbilical supplies breathing gas, hot water for his suit, communications, depth gauge and television cable, thus the diver in the bell can control how much umbilical is paid out, under the direct instructions of the diving supervisor. In this incident, too much umbilical was paid out and it fouled a turning propeller, which reeled the diver in and killed him. It was a fundamental breach of safety rules and could have been avoided. This was complicated in that the substantive evidence showing that the supervisor had ordered the umbilical to be paid out had been deliberately removed from the 'black box' video.

The first task for the HSE Inspectors was to prepare the initial investigation report with recommendations for enforcement action. The Inspectors found serious breaches of safety procedures, which were both industry and company accepted and adopted. The breaches were so serious that it had been identified that an individual and the company were seriously negligent and there were considerations for both individual manslaughter and corporate manslaughter. The Coroner had requested a copy of the report and acting upon the findings submitted his report to the Department of Public Prosecutions (DPP) with the recommendations of proceedings for manslaughter. Within ten days, the DPP's office had agreed with the recommendations, had passed the file to the CPS who in turn had appointed a Special Casework Lawyer. The police were instructed to investigate. The HSE Inspectors were very much aware that the case was no longer under the control of the HSE, but they had a vital contribution to make if an effective case was to be brought.

The first meeting was with the Detective Sergeant (DS) who was to lead the police investigation and at that point they sorted out the ground rules. The HSE inspectors knew virtually nothing about police procedures and the police knew even less about health and safety and corporate management matters. From that first meeting it was agreed that all parties would combine efforts, using the police phrase, 'to get a result'. This was vital as experience shows that often when different organisations combine there are conflicts of personalities, and the objective becomes secondary. Everybody concerned were all determined that was not going to occur in this instance and the HSE case manager took it upon himself to become the 'case manager' without portfolio.

The next meeting was with the CPS lawyer, who was a team player, involving everybody concerned in round-table discussions on every aspect of the case and investigation. Questions, no matter how obscure, were dealt with by explanation, and this meant that everybody learnt and understood what was happening. It was important that when counsel was appointed he was also a team player, drawing in views and opinions from everybody involved. Internal support came from the then HSE head of litigation on health and safety legal issues and guidance for the HSE expert witness. The PACE (Police and Criminal Evidence Act 1984 Code of Practice) and section 9 interviews were undertaken by a combination of police and HSE, the DS with the police system for handling evidence, took on the mantle of exhibits officer.

The most difficult aspect of running a case of this type was that there were four separate elements, the HSE, police, CPS and counsel, all of whom were very busy and all important to the process. There were meetings, interviews and visits to be undertaken, many of which involved individuals and companies. The Norfolk Constabulary had to liaise with their counterparts in Scotland, and that required co-operation as PACE statements were taken at an Aberdeen Police station, and required the Aberdeen Police to enforce a warrant on the individual defendant. Throughout this time, the HSE administrator took on the task of planner and organiser playing a vital role in keeping the case preparation on time and within a reasonable budget as well as keeping contact with witnesses as the trial date approached.

The most difficult task was to undertake a visit to the Diving Support Vessel which only enters port to take on fuel, provisions and equipment, giving very narrow windows of opportunity. After a number of false starts, a provisional date was given and the prosecution team put on stand-by. The vessel would enter the port of Leith (Edinburgh) allowing the prosecution and defence teams onboard. After eleventh hour adjustments to the plan, everybody who wanted to be onboard was, and the task of inspecting the site of the incident and videoing the key aspects of the vessel and its equipment were completed. Without the multi-team management and co-operation this visit would never have occurred.

Another challenge that the team faced was that people had moved on to other work sites, which can be expected in the oil and gas industry because it is global in nature. That meant tracing people overseas to obtain information and sign statements. The individual defendant had passports from Britain, South Africa and Zimbabwe, and was, during the investigation and pre-trial phase, working in the Middle East. Another key prosecution witness was working in Vietnam and another witness was in Canada. Again, as a team all objectives were achieved with everybody in court when required. The question at the forefront of the prosecution team's thoughts was to determine who was to be prosecuted and with what offences. After lengthy consideration it was accepted by all that an individual would be charged with manslaughter and perverting the course of justice. The only differences of opinion within the prosecution team were in respect to the charges to be laid against the company. The HSE, police and counsel supported a corporate manslaughter charge, but the CPS put forward an argument against, based upon the previous failures in corporate manslaughter cases where large corporations were involved. (Problems regarding the P&O European Ferries/*Herald of Free Enterprise* case have been examined in Chapter 2.) After much debate, both within the prosecution team and within the CPS, it was reluctantly decided that the company would only be charged with health and safety offences.

Two years after the fatal incident the case went to trial. The company pleaded guilty to two health and safety charges and the individual pleaded not guilty to manslaughter and perverting the course of justice but guilty under HASWA 1974, s 7. It is worthy of note that the HSE diving inspectors faced 'public' criticism and that while the diving supervisor was charged with the serious offence, the company was seen to 'have got away with it'. It was very evident that in the minds of the 'public', health and safety offences were not considered serious compared with manslaughter, which was a very different option.

At trial the prosecution team had to be prepared for all eventualities and quirks in the judicial system. In the opening phase of the case, the judge questioned why the case was in a criminal court and not in the civil court. He considered it to be a civil matter, in other words, it was a matter of compensation. He was concerned that an individual was in the 'dock' on serious charges and the company was not. Furthermore, the judge decided that because it was not really a criminal case he allowed the defendant to sit with his defence team and not in the dock.

The outcome of the three-week trial was that the individual was found not guilty of manslaughter, based primarily on the fact that the company's safety management system fell far short of what could be reasonably expected, and that the individual defendant was part of that system. As a result of the summing up of the case, the jury would not place the whole burden on an individual. He was found guilty of perverting the course of justice and received a one-month custodial sentence. He was fined £500 for the section 7 offence under the HSAWA 1974. The company, who had made guilty pleas, provided first class mitigation but were fined £100,000 for each offence, and with a contribution of prosecution costs faced a figure of £225,000, which reflected the seriousness the judge placed upon the company's part in the incident.

A number of issues flowed from this case, the first being that the three groups, the HSE, police and the CPS, followed the spirit of the new 'Work Related Deaths – A Protocol for Liaison', even though at the time it was only in the process of drafting. What is clear is that if adopted by all involved, it will work, and work effectively. It was also very evident in hindsight that the prosecution should have proceeded with a charge of corporate manslaughter and tempted providence.

What of the future? The case that has been discussed involved a company that had been prosecuted previously but had been found not guilty. Management failure was evident in both cases but no lessons had been learned from the first case. Serious consideration was given to corporate manslaughter charges but because of the current law the CPS would not pursue that avenue. In the wider view, that is emphasised by the pressure from relatives, survivors and the general public who demand that directors of corporations should be held accountable for safety failures, and that means a change in the law.

The argument has been made as to why the new offence is required. The HSE already has section 37 of the HSWA 1974 which deals with the body corporate. However, offences under the HSWA 1974 are not considered by many to be 'criminal', such as, for example, robbery, theft, or an act involving violence and, therefore, do not generally receive the attention from the courts that may be expected. This is further supported in that a prosecution under HASWA 1974, s 37 draws little or no emotion, however, the mention of corporate killing awakens even the most disinterested. One held perception is that directors could go to prison for a corporate killing offence which is the outcome generally sought by 'public' opinion. However, the proposed penalty for this offence is a fine against the company and that creates other problems such as limited resources to pay a substantial fine, the transfer of assets and companies being wound up prior to the trial. The response from the 'public' is that any outcome of a corporate killing case must provide a suitable punishment while posing a deterrent to others. It is also very relevant that major corporations have the financial resources to mount a defence where they pay and play to win.

The offence of corporate killing will be directed at safety failures involving death at work, but there are concerns which involve cases where there have been serious safety failings with an identifiable potential for loss of life but, by good fortune, there have been no deaths. It is evident that in these cases the penalty should reflect the seriousness of the offence, however, opponents of corporate killing will argue that this is not the situation at present. The offence of corporate killing will be an important and valuable tool in the legal system for those occasions when it is required. It will involve the HSE to be involved with remedial orders made by a court so as to ensure that they are reasonable, and in line with the HSC Enforcement Policy Statement and what is regarded as good practice. An offence of this type will allow the courts to identify the seriousness of health and safety offences and reflect it in the penalty.

The new protocol for liaison

6.4 As part of the developing process to ensure effective investigation and legal process of accidents involving a death at work, the HSE, the Association of Chief Police Officers (ACPO), the British Transport Police (BTP), the Local Government Association and the CPS have become signatories to a formal protocol for liaison. The protocol sets out the principles for effective liaison between the parties in relation to work-related deaths in England and Wales and is available to the public. Information drawn from the document entitled 'Work-Related Deaths, a Protocol for Liaison' (MISC491) is published by the HSE. In particular, it deals with incidents where, following a death, evidence indicates that a serious criminal offence other than a health and safety offence may have been committed to determine if there is evidence that there may be a case of individual or corporate manslaughter.

The five signatories to the protocol have different roles and responsibilities where there has been a work related death. The HSE functions include enforcing compliance within the scope of the Health and Safety at Work Act 1974, but it cannot investigate or prosecute for general criminal offences, including manslaughter. HSE and local authorities are responsible, under section 18 of the Health and Safety at Work etc Act 1974, for making adequate arrangements for the enforcement of health and safety legislation with a view to securing the health, safety and welfare of workers and protecting others, principally the public. Each has specific areas of responsibility.

At present, only the police can investigate serious criminal offences (other than health and safety offences) such as manslaughter, and only the CPS can decide whether such a case will proceed. The police will also have a role in establishing the circumstances surrounding a work-related death in order to assist the coroner's inquest. Health and safety offences are usually prosecuted by HSE, the local authority or other enforcing authority in accordance with current enforcement policy. However, the CPS may also prosecute health and safety offences, but usually does so only when prosecuting other serious criminal offences, such as manslaughter or perverting the course of justice, arising out of the same incident.

When making a decision whether to prosecute, the CPS, HSE, the local authority or other enforcing authority will review the evidence according to the Code for Crown prosecutors to decide if there is a realistic prospect of conviction and, if so, whether a prosecution is needed in the public interest. The underlying principles of this protocol are as follows:

- an appropriate decision concerning prosecution will be made based on a sound investigation of the circumstances surrounding work-related deaths;

- the police will conduct an investigation where there is an indication of the commission of a serious criminal offence (other than a health and safety offence), and the HSE, the local authority or other enforcing authority will investigate health and safety offences. There will usually be a joint investigation, but on the rare occasions where this would not be appropriate, there will still be liaison and co-operation between the investigating parties;

- the decision to prosecute will be co-ordinated and made without undue delay;

- the bereaved and witnesses will be kept suitably informed; and

- parties to the protocol will maintain effective mechanisms for liaison.

A work-related death is a fatality resulting from an incident arising out of, or in connection with, work. However, the principles set out in this protocol also apply to cases where the victim suffers injuries in such an incident that are so serious that there is a clear indication, according to medical opinion, of a strong likelihood of death.

It is inevitable that there will be cases in which it is difficult to determine whether a death is work-related within the application of this protocol. Therefore, every fatality must be considered individually, on its particular facts and a decision made as to whether it should be classed as a work-related death. In determining the question, the enforcing authorities will hold discussions and agree upon a conclusion without delay.

In the early stages of an investigation, it is not always apparent that a serious criminal offence has been committed and those responsible for the investigation must ensure that any investigation into a work-related death is thorough and appropriate, and agree to work closely together in order to achieve this. Decisions in relation to who will lead the investigation and the direction it will take will need to be made as a matter of urgency involving the best available evidence and technical expertise. If there are any issues as to who is to be involved in investigating any work-related death, then those involved will have to work together to reach a rapid conclusion.

A police officer will generally be the first at the site as the HSE or local government are not an emergency service and will dispatch an inspector as soon as is possible. It is important that a police officer attending an incident involving a work-related death follow the following guidelines according to the officer's own force procedures:

- identify, secure, preserve and take control of the scene, and any other relevant place;

- supervise and record all activity;

- inform a senior supervisory officer;

- enquire whether the employer or other responsible person in control of the premises or activity has informed HSE, the local authority or other investigating or enforcing authority; and

- contact and discuss the incident with HSE, the local authority or other enforcing authority, and agree arrangements for controlling the scene, for considering access to others, and for other local handling procedures to ensure the safety of the public.

Because of the seriousness of a potential manslaughter prosecution, and the need to preserve evidence, a police officer of supervisory rank should attend the scene and any other relevant place to assess the situation, review actions taken to date and assume responsibility for the investigation. Should any other investigating or enforcing authority have staff at the scene before the police arrive, the inspectors should ensure that the police have been called and preserve the scene until the police get there.

The protocol requires the investigations to be managed professionally, with communications between the signatory organisations continually maintained. Generally, investigations should be jointly conducted, with one of the parties taking the lead, or primacy, as appropriate. An investigation may also require liaison with any other enforcing authority that may have an interest, and may include liaison with the CPS. Throughout the period of the investigation, the police and HSE, the local authority or other enforcing authority will need to keep the progress of the investigation under review. This can be achieved through milestones which should be agreed and monitored, and policy and key decisions recorded.

With a workplace fatality, the police, HSE, the local authority or other enforcing authority should agree upon:

- how resources are to be specifically used;

- how evidence is to be disclosed between the parties;

- how the interviewing of witnesses, the instruction of experts and the forensic examination of exhibits is to be co-ordinated;

- how, and to what extent, corporate or organisational failures should be investigated;

- a strategy for keeping the bereaved, witnesses, and other interested parties such as the coroner, informed of developments in the investigation; and

- a media strategy to take account of the sensitivities of the bereaved and those involved in the incident, and to encourage consistency of approach in reporting.

In certain large-scale investigations a strategic liaison group may be established to ensure effective inter-organisational communication, and to share relevant information and experiences. Where the investigation gives rise to a suspicion that a serious criminal offence (other than a health and safety offence) may have caused the death, the police will assume primacy for the investigation and will work in partnership with HSE, the local authority or other enforcing authority. Where it becomes apparent during the investigation that there is insufficient evidence that a serious criminal offence (other than a health and safety offence) caused the death, the investigation should, by agreement, be taken over by the HSE, the local authority or other enforcing authority with both parties should record such a decision in writing. Where the HSE, the local authority or other enforcing authority is investigating the death, and new information is discovered, it may move the level of seriousness up to a level where the police need to consider the new evidence to determine whether a serious criminal offence (other than a health and safety offence) has been committed. The police will then consider whether to resume primacy for the investigation and that decision with reasons should be recorded in writing.

There will also be rare occasions where as a result of the Coroner's inquest, judicial review or other legal proceedings, that further consideration of the evidence and surrounding facts may need to be made. Where this takes place, the police, the enforcing authority with primacy for the investigation and the CPS will work in partnership to ensure an early decision. There may also be a need for further investigation.

Where there has been an investigation, any material obtained should be shared, subject to any legal restrictions, between the police, the HSE, the local authority or other enforcing authority and the CPS. For the purpose of continuity, special handling procedures may be necessary and the organisation responsible for retaining the exhibits, documents and other relevant material should also be agreed upon.

In the case of some incidents, particularly those involving multiple fatalities, the HSC may, with the consent of the Secretary of State, direct that a public inquiry be held. Alternatively, the Commission may authorise the HSE, or any other person, to investigate and produce a special report. In such circumstances, the police will provide any necessary support and evidence to the person appointed to conduct the public inquiry, or to the special investigation, subject to the relevant regulations.

Complex legal issues may arise when there are parallel public inquiries and criminal investigations or prosecutions. The signatories will aim to keep inquiry chairs informed of the progress of the investigation. Sometimes the report of a public inquiry may be delayed to await the conclusion of criminal proceedings and, on other occasions, there may be no such delay because of strong public interest in publishing the report and the recommendations of a public inquiry quickly. In either event, the signatories to the protocol will work together to ensure that the decision to prosecute is made as expeditiously as possible and any criminal proceedings commenced without delay.

Early liaison by the police, the HSE, the local authority or other enforcing authority with the CPS is important and there is no need to wait until a file is ready to be submitted before the police open discussions with the CPS. The police are encouraged, at any stage following a work-related death, to consult the CPS for advice, not only about the nature of any charges, but also as to the legal and evidential issues surrounding the investigation, including advice about expert evidence. It follows that the police should seek the advice of the CPS before charging an individual with any serious criminal offence (other than a health and safety offence) arising out of a work-related death.

The police must consult the CPS Casework Directorate for advice when there is any consideration of charging a company or corporation with any serious criminal offence (other than a health and safety offence). The decision to prosecute will be taken by the CPS according to 'The Code for Crown Prosecutors'. Such an offence may be prosecuted either with or without related health and safety offences. The decision will be made following discussion with the police, and, where appropriate, the HSE, the local authority or another enforcing authority. There should be no undue delay in reaching the prosecution decision. If there is a delay, then the CPS will notify the police and the enforcing authority and explain the reasons for the delay, and will keep them informed of the progress of the decision making. Of importance, the CPS should always take into account the consequences for the bereaved of the decision whether or not to prosecute, and of any views expressed by them.

When the CPS has made its decision, it must be communicated to the police, HSE, the local authority or other enforcing authority as soon as practicable, so that the HSE, the local authority or other enforcing authority can decide as expeditiously as possible whether to prosecute for health and safety offences if the CPS is not doing so. A decision not to prosecute will have to be made public until the bereaved, the Coroner's Office and any potential defendants have been notified according to the previously agreed strategy. Where there is to be no CPS prosecution, the announcement of the CPS's decision shall include the fact that the decision of the HSE, the local authority or other enforcing authority will be made after the inquest. Of particular importance to the bereaved is the CPS policy to set out its reasons in writing and send them to the bereaved, and to offer to meet them to discuss the reasons for reaching the decision.

Where the CPS, the HSE and the local authority or another enforcing authority seek to prosecute offences arising out of the same incident, the prosecution(s) shall be initiated and managed jointly. There should be an early conference attended by the CPS, the police and HSE, the local authority or other enforcing authority to consider the management of the proceedings. In particular, the following issues should be discussed, agreed and recorded:

- who will take lead responsibility for the prosecution;

- the nature and the wording of the charges (including, where appropriate, consideration of any alternative charges and acceptable pleas);

- arrangements for the retention and disclosure of material;

- a case management timetable;

- arrangements for keeping the bereaved and witnesses informed;

- the announcement of the decision;

- arrangements for maintaining contact during the prosecution, and an agreement as to a mechanism for consulting, should an issue arise which results in the discontinuance of the proceedings or no evidence being offered;

- an agreement as to any specific instructions to the prosecuting advocate; and

- any other case management issues.

The police or the CPS will notify the coroner when a serious criminal offence arising out of a work-related death (other than a health and safety offence) has been charged. The coroner may then adjourn the inquest until the end of the criminal prosecution and the Director of Public Prosecutions may also ask the coroner to adjourn the inquest. Where the CPS has reviewed the case and decided not to prosecute, the HSE, the local authority or other enforcing authority will have to await the result of the coroner's inquest before charging any health and safety offences, unless to wait would prejudice the case. Where, following an inquest, public inquiry, judicial review or other legal proceedings, it is necessary for the CPS to review or re-review the case, the HSE, the local authority or other enforcing authority will wait until the review by the CPS has been completed before instigating or continuing its own proceedings.

A National Liaison Committee comprises representatives from the police, BTP, the CPS, the HSE and the Local Government Association and will meet at least twice a year to review the operation of the protocol and consider the need for changes to the arrangements. Regional Liaison Committees comprise representatives from the signatories, nominated at local levels. These committees will meet on a regular basis to discuss issues of mutual interest and concern and, in particular, the operation of the protocol from a local standpoint, to monitor the protocol's effectiveness, and to communicate any issues to the National Liaison Committee. The Regional Liaison Committees will be responsible for ensuring that there is an identified and effective line of local communication between the five organisations.

Enforcement of the HSWA 1974 and the related legislation is generally shared between the HSE and local authorities. A general guide to the allocation of the main activity is detailed below.

The Health and Safety Executive (HSE)

6.5   The HSE is responsible for enforcing work-related health and safety legislation in the following:

'factories and other manufacturing premises, including motor vehicle repair; chemical plants and refineries; construction; railways, tram and underground systems; mines, quarries and landfill sites; farms, agriculture and forestry; hospitals, including nursing homes; local government, including their offices and facilities run by them; schools, colleges and universities; domestic gas installation, maintenance or repair; utilities, including power generation, water, and waste; fairgrounds (traveling or fixed); airports (except terminal buildings, car parks and office buildings); police and fire authorities; Crown bodies, including the Ministry of Defence; prisons; docks; nuclear installations; offshore gas and oil installations and associated activities, including pipe-laying barges and diving support vessels; onshore major hazards, including pipelines, gas transmission and distribution; transport of dangerous goods by road and rail; manufacture, transport, handling and security of explosives; common parts of domestic premises'.

In England and Wales, local authorities enforce the HSWA 1974 in respect of certain non-domestic premises, including:

'shops and retailing, including market stalls, coin-operated launderettes, and mobile vendors; most office-based activities; some wholesale and retail warehouses; hotels, guest houses, hostels, caravan and camping sites, restaurants, public houses and other licensed premises; leisure and entertainment, including night clubs, cinemas, social clubs, circuses, sports facilities, health clubs, gyms, riding schools, racecourses, pleasure boat hire, motor-racing circuits, museums, theatres, art galleries and exhibition centers; places of worship and undertakers; animal care, including zoos, livery stables and kennels; therapeutic and beauty services, including massage, saunas, solariums, tattooing, skin and body piercing, and hairdressing; residential care homes; privately run pre-school child care, eg nurseries'.

It is important to remember that the HSE is not an emergency service. It has produced guidance for police and other emergency service control rooms describing how to contact HSE inspectors out of hours. There will be local arrangements in place for contacting the authorised health and safety inspectors within local authorities.

➢ **Help Point:** 'The Work-Related Deaths, a Protocol for Liaison' is published by the Health and Safety Executive. For further information telephone the HSE's Infoline on 08701 545500 or e-mail hseinformationservices@natbtrit.com or write to HSE Information Services, Caerphilly Business Park, Caerphilly BF83 3GG. CPS publications are available from CPS Communications Branch, 50 Ludgate Hill, London, EC4M 7EX; telephone 020 7796 8442; website: www.cps.gov.uk The ACPO website: www.acpo.police.uk

Legal considerations

6.6 A major factor arising from prosecutions of undertakings is that of consistency in the numerous courts and the level of information about the undertaking that had been provided. The cases of *R v Howe & Son (Engineers) Ltd [1999] 2 Cr App R (S) 37* and *R v Friskies Petcare (UK) Ltd [2000] Cr App R (S) 401* have been identified as providing the basis for consideration by the court when determining the level of fines to be imposed. The cases are summarised below.

Howe & Son Ltd

6.7 Problems that have occurred with health and safety prosecutions have been the lack of consistency in case preparation and presentation as well as the courts determination as to the level of penalties to impose. This resulted in a variance throughout the country and from case to case, with some cases involving loss of life receiving fines lower than cases where there had been no loss of life. The situation changed when *Howe & Son* pleaded guilty on 10 November 1997 at Bristol Crown Court to four offences and was fined: £40,000 for a breach of section 2(1) of the HSWA 1974, for failing to ensure the safety of its employees as far as was reasonably practicable; £2,000 under reg 4(2) of the Electricity at Work Regulations 1989 (SI 1989/635), for failing to maintain an electric cable to a machine; £2,000 under reg 3 of the Management of Health and Safety at Work Regulations 1992 (SI 1992/2051), for failing to make a suitable and sufficient risk assessment; £4,000 under the Electricity at Work Regulations 1989 for failing to ensure that means were provided to protect the electrical system supplying the machine from excess current. This amounted to a fine of £48,000. In addition the defendants were ordered to pay £7,500 costs.

The case involved Giles Smith, aged 20, who was electrocuted on 13 August 1996 while cleaning Howe & Son's factory, which had been shut down for the purpose. The cleaning process involved water that was collected by an electric vacuum machine, which had been bought second-hand at an auction in 1995. The investigation found that the cable to the machine became trapped between one of its wheels and the floor, damaging the cable and making the machine live. Smith, who was holding the machine, was unable to let it go until the power was turned off. He was taken to hospital, where he was certified dead.

Aggravating/mitigating factors

6.8   The Court of Appeal set out the criteria of identifying mitigating and aggravating factors that judges should take into account when fixing the level of a fine. The court found that the trial judge had given insufficient weight to the company's financial position when sentencing, and addressed the situation by reducing the fine from £48,000 to £15,000.

The Court of Appeal established its sentencing comments on the following criteria:

> 'The objective of prosecutions for health and safety offences in the workplace is to achieve a safe environment for those who work there and for other members of the public who may be affected. A fine needs to be large enough to bring that message home where the defendant is a company not only to those who manage it but also to its shareholders ... fines should not be so large as to imperil the earnings of employees or create a risk of bankruptcy ... there might be cases where the offences are so serious that the defendant ought not to be in business ... it is impossible to lay down any tariff or to say that the fine should bear any specific relationship to the turnover or net profit of the defendant ... The Court split the 'relevant factors' that judges and magistrates should consider when setting a fine into three categories – criteria, other matters, and mitigating and aggravating factors'.

The criteria categories include the following.

(a)   *Failure* – 'In assessing the gravity of the breach, it is often helpful to look at how far short of the right standard the defendant fell in failing to meet the "reasonably practicable" test.'

(b)   *Death* – 'It is often a matter of chance whether death or serious injury results from even a serious breach. Generally where death is the consequence of a criminal act, it is regarded as an aggravating feature of the offence. The penalty should reflect public disquiet at the unnecessary loss of life.'

(c)   *Profit* –'A deliberate breach of health and safety legislation with a view to profit seriously aggravates the offence'. The court stated: 'Financial profit can often be made at the expense of [protecting] employees and the public'.

(d)   *Size* – Although this will affect the level of the fine, the court of Appeal emphasised that: 'the standard of care imposed by the legislation is the same regardless of the size of the company ... The size of a company and its financial strength or weakness cannot affect the degree of care that is required in matters of safety. That said, how individual company's discharge their duties depends on the circumstances'.

It was identified that there may be other matters that may affect the sentence and include:

'The degree of risk and extent of the danger created by the offence; The extent of the breach whether the failure was an isolated incident or continued over a period; and importantly, the defendant's resources and the effect of the fine on its business.'

In addition, the court identified particular aggravating and mitigating features:

1.   *aggravating* factors include:

(a)   a failure to heed warnings; and

(b)   where the defendant has deliberately profited financially from a failure to take necessary health and safety steps or run a risk to save money;

2.   *mitigating* factors include:

(a)   prompt admission of responsibility and a timely plea of guilt;

(b)   steps to remedy deficiencies after they are drawn to the defendant's attention; and

(c)   a good safety record.

The first factor involves the aggravating features, which included:

- it was not a one-off failure but a failure over many months;

- the case was very serious, involving a fatality; and

- there was a failure to recognise the significance of, and deal with, previous adverse events.

To counter the aggravating aspects of the case, the mitigating features included:

- the companies had pleaded guilty at the earliest opportunity; and

- they had co-operated with the HSE to ensure that the problems had been rectified.

The Friskies judgment

6.9 When preparing a case for prosecution the regulating authorities carry out a 'Friskies' assessment to identify the aggravating and mitigating features of the defendant and submit the information as part of the prosecution bundle. This will provide the court with important information to aid them when determining the sentence. The case that brought about this change in procedure was *R v Friskies Petcare (UK) Ltd.*

The company was fined £600,000 at Isleworth Crown Court after the electrocution of an employee in a meat silo at their factory at Southall, West London. Bryan Wilkins was repairing a metal ribbon stirrer at the bottom of the silo. He was arc welding in a confined, damp conductive environment in the silo when he was electrocuted while changing welding electrodes.

The company pleaded guilty to breach of section 2 of the HSWA 1974, and regulation 3 of the Management of Health & Safety at Work Regulations 1992, for failing to ensure, so far as was reasonably practicable, the safety of employees, including Bryan Wilkins, whilst arc welding in metal meat silos. They also pleaded guilty to breach of regulation 3 of the Management of Health & Safety at Work Regulations 1992 for failing to make a suitable and sufficient assessment of the risks to their employees, including Bryan Wilkins, to which they were exposed whilst arc welding in metal meat silos for the purpose of identifying the measures needed to comply with the relevant statutory requirements. The company appealed against the level of fine and the Court of Appeal subsequently reduced it to £250,000.

The company appealed against the level of fine.

The fine was reduced by the Court of Appeal in March 2000. This decision was made on the grounds that the trial judge had incorrectly included an 'aggravating' factor after he had erroneously found that the company had put profit before safety. It is considered that a deliberate breach of health and safety legislation with a view to profit seriously aggravates the offence. The court stated that 'financial profit can often be made at the expense of protecting employees and the public'. It was not disputed in court when the company claimed that there was no evidence of cost cutting for financial gain. The Court of Appeal judgment reinforced the sentencing criteria established in *Howe*, and identified that fines of £500,000 and above tend to be reserved for those cases where a major public disaster occurs. It can be anticipated that fines for corporate killing offences will be at the highest level. The court also provided guidance to the HSE and defendants about how they should prepare and present mitigating and aggravating factors to the trial court which would allow all factors to be considered.

It was found that the Crown Court had made an error in finding the existence of the aggravating feature – profit – which meant that the fine of £600,000 took into account a factor that it should not have.

Aggravating/mitigating factors

6.10   The court found that the *aggravating* factors were:

- the death of Mr Wilkins;

- the position of the switch for turning off the current, which was too inaccessible should anything go wrong;

- the fact that the breaches had been going on for some time;

- none of the employees had their attention drawn to HSE guidance on welding;

- the firm had conducted no assessment of the risk involved in repairing ribbon stirrers in situ;

- the incident represented a serious and obvious breach of duty.

The *mitigating* factors for the company were;

- a prompt admission and plea of guilty;

- a good health and safety record over the years;

- the steps the company had taken since the incident to improve safety, all of which had been taken with the approval of, and confirmation by, the HSE and which now agreed that Friskies had 'a high level of commitment to safety'.

The Court of Appeal also took into account the financial position of the company, which it described as a very substantial business with a considerable turnover, generating pre-tax profits at the relevant time of some £40m. The court, therefore, reduced the fine from £600,000 to £250,000. However, it refused to allow Friskies costs from central funds.

Observers may consider that the company took steps after the incident to improve safety and submitted this as mitigation as opposed to adopting safety procedures before an incident. It may also be considered that the fine was reduced too low when balanced against the company's profit and original fine. Further, the offence was committed over a considerable period of time. It may also be argued that some undertakings put profit at the top of their operating activities, and there was no difference in this case because it was only luck that there had not been an accident earlier.

The considerations above are important factors for legal debate, but the *Friskies* judgment does focus the minds of the regulating authorities when investigating an incident and preparing the case for trial before the courts. This will be an equally important aspect when preparing a case for a corporate killing offence prosecution. This case should also serve as a warning to all undertakings to place health and safety at the top of the management agenda because the fine, prosecution costs, defence legal costs and remedial action costs show that it would have been more financially effective to adopt safety management procedures in the first place.

R v Janway Davies

6.11 A major milestone in health and safety law was attained when three Appeal judges ruled on an appeal between David Janway Davies and the HSE (*R v Janway Davies (2003) CA IRLR 170*). The appeal was in respect to section 40 of the Health and Safety at Work etc Act 1974 where the court had to consider whether a reversal of the burden of proof provision in a statute creating offences is compatible with the presumption of innocence enshrined in Article 6(2) of the European Convention on Human Rights (ECHR). The statute in question is the Health and Safety at Work Act 1974. The combined effect of sections 3(1) and 33(1) of the Act make it an offence for an employer to fail to discharge:

'the duty to conduct his undertaking in such a way as to ensure, so far as is reasonably practicable, that persons not in his employment who may be affected thereby are not thereby exposed to risks to their health or safety'.

Section 40 provides that in any proceedings for an offence:

'consisting of a failure to comply with a duty ... to do something ... so far as is reasonably practicable ... it shall be for the accused to prove ... that it was not reasonably practicable to do more than was in fact done to satisfy the duty'.

The facts of the case involves Davies who ran a plant hire firm from a yard and workshop near Neath where he had three employees and employed three self-employed subcontractors, one of whom was Mr Gardner. On 25 January 2000, Gardner returned to the yard at about 3.30 pm and asked Davies if there was any further work for him to do. At the time, Davies was in the workshop working on a Volvo dumper truck when he told Gardner that he should go home and then shouted to an employee, Mr Ralph, who was in the yard, to bring a JCB down into the workshop and park it tight up to the dumper. Ralph, complying with the instruction, reversed the JCB with its lights flashing down into the open workshop. It was as he approached the truck that he had to retract the machine's rear arm which left him with very little visibility to the rear. Ralph did not see Gardner, who was then crushed between the two vehicles, sustaining fatal injuries. Davies had resumed working in the cab of the truck, and some time before the accident he noticed that Gardner had not left the workshop but he did not see the accident itself.

The outcome of the prosecution of Davies, which was heard in the Swansea Crown Court, was a conviction on 7 September 2001 for an offence under the HSWA 1974. He was fined £15,000 and ordered to pay £22,544 prosecution costs. At the close of the prosecution case, the judge (Judge Price QC) ruled that section 40 of the HSWA 1974 was compatible with the ECHR and, therefore, directed the jury that there was a legal (persuasive) burden on Davies to prove (on the balance of probability) that it was not reasonably practicable for him to do more than he had in fact done. Davies based his appeal on this point, contending that section 40 of the HSWA 1974 is only compatible if it imposes an evidential burden. This appeal was of great importance because it affects prosecutions for a number of offences under the Act and there are conflicting decisions at Crown Court level.

The court concluded that the imposition of a legal burden of proof under section 40 of the Act is justified, necessary and proportionate for the reasons set out below which take account of the various points:

> 'First the Act is regulatory and its purpose is to protect the health and safety of those affected by the activities referred to in sections 2 to 6. The need for such regulation is amply demonstrated by the statistics with which we have been supplied. These show that fatal injuries reported to the UK enforcing authorities by industry are running at an average of about 700 a year and non-fatal major injuries at nearly 200,000 a year. Following a survey in 1995/96 the Office of Statistics put the financial costs of accidents at work in the UK at between £14.5 and £18.1 billion. The Act's purpose is therefore both social and economic'.

The court continued to state:

> 'The reversal of the burden of proof takes into account the fact that duty holders are persons who have chosen to engage in work or commercial activity (probably for gain) and are in charge of it. They are not, therefore, unengaged or disinterested members of the public and in choosing to operate in a regulated sphere of activity they must be taken to have accepted the regulatory controls that go with it. This regulatory regime imposes a continuing duty to ensure a state of affairs, a safety standard. Where the enforcing authority can show that this has not been achieved it is not

unjustifiable or unfair to ask the duty holder who has either created or is in control of the risk to show that it was not reasonably practicable for him to have done more than he did to prevent or avoid it ... Before any question of reverse onus arises the prosecution must prove that the defendant owes the duty (in the case of section 3 to the person affected by the conduct of his undertaking) and that the safety standard (in the case of section 3 exposure to risk to health or safety) has been breached. Proof of these matters is not a formality ... There may be real issues about whether the defendant owes the relevant duty or whether in fact the safety standard has been breached, for example, where the cause of an accident is unknown or debatable. But once the prosecution, have proved these matters the defence has to be raised and established by the defendant. The defence itself is flexible because it does not restrict the way in which the defendant can show that he has done what is reasonably practicable'.

Clarity was given with regard to the application of reverse onus and the judgment identified:

'The reverse onus only applies to breach of the duties laid down by sections 2 to 6 of the Act. It does not apply section 7, so there is no reverse onus of proof where it is alleged that an employee has breached his duty. The same applies to section 37 where a company's officers may be convicted if the company has committed an offence and they are proved to have consented, connived or contributed to it by neglect. This suggests that Parliament must have considered when a reverse onus was justified and when it was not. Due regard must be paid to its choice'.

The defence is a critical issue and the judgment addressed the issue through the following statement:

'The facts relied on in support of the defence should not be difficult to prove because they will be within the knowledge of the defendant. Whether the defendant should have done more will be judged objectively. If all the defendant had to do was raise the defence to require the prosecution to disprove it, the focus of the statutory scheme would be changed. The trial would become focused on what it was the enforcing authority was saying should have been done rather than on what the defendant had done or ought to have done which is what Parliament intended. In complicated, and therefore potentially the most serious, cases the prosecution might face considerable difficulties in assuming this burden of proof where the only relevant expertise was with the defendant or even its state of the art supplier or licensor abroad. In such cases, therefore, enforcement might become impossible if the defendant only had an evidential burden'.

The court in its concluding decisions stated:

'Last but not least the defendant in cases where the reverse burden of proof applies does not face imprisonment. The offence involves failure to comply with an objective standard. The consequences of such failure may be newsworthy in some cases but the moral obloquy is not the same as that involved in truly criminal offences. The statistics we have been provided with show that only about 15% of those prosecuted under sections 2 to 6 of the Act are individuals. The rest are companies. For these reasons we think the judge reached the right conclusion in this case. The reverse legal burden of proof contained in section 40 of the Act is compatible with the ECHR. The appellant's conviction on this basis was not therefore unsafe'.

In respect to the importance of this judgement, it is equal to that of the *Howe* and *Friskies* judgements for both the prosecution and defendants in health and safety prosecutions.

Those having read the details of the three cases will know that there are considerations within the legal system that clarify some fundamental situations upon which any court can set basic principles. This aids the prosecution in its preparation for prosecution and makes the position clear for the defence. It also sets the scene for both the magistrates and judge upon which they can make sound decisions.

The Scottish legal system

6.12   Scotland has its own legal process but, in practice, similar procedures are adopted. There are no Magistrates' courts in Scotland and so the Sheriff's court combines the functions of the Crown and Magistrates' courts in England and Wales. Criminal prosecutions may be tried in the Sheriff's court, either on indictment before a Sheriff and jury or on summary before a Sheriff sitting alone.

In Scotland there are no Coroner's courts and inquests as such are not held. The Fatal Accident and Sudden Death (Scotland) Act 1976 requires that the Procurator Fiscal for a district will investigate the circumstances, and apply to the Sheriff for the holding of an inquiry into a death. The death will be arising as a result of an accident in Scotland while the deceased was at work, either as an employee or self employed.

There are two exceptions to this rule: an enquiry does not need to be held in cases where criminal proceedings have been concluded against any person in respect of the death; or where, in any work-related accident which resulted in a death, the Lord Advocate is satisfied that the circumstances of the death have been sufficiently established.

Chapter 7

How to Manage Contractors Safely

Introduction

7.0   While it is possible to contract out some, or all, of the work activities of a company, it is impossible to contract out any responsibilities to care for all parties at the worksite and this means that everybody has some responsibility for health and safety. The client must provide full information relating to health and safety requirements and they must ensure that the contractor can meet those requirements. Contracting has become the principal method of working in the UK which means that more companies could have their registered address located outside the jurisdiction of UK courts. This can leave UK clients exposed if there are accidents or incidents as they cannot absolve their responsibilities. This chapter considers how subcontracted activities and workscopes can be effectively managed with examples of what can go wrong if not properly managed.

Modern business operations

7.1   In recent years there have been major changes evolving in the structure of modern businesses. Companies have reduced staff numbers through downsizing and many of the functions previously conducted in-house are now outsourced. This means that much of the work bought in involves specialist contractors, small contractors or self-employed persons.

The HSE defines the use of contractors as:

> 'the process of restructuring or other initiatives carried out by an organisation to enable contractors to be used to replace or augment directly employed staff in performing functions'.

In addition to employing contractors, many organisations have introduced partnering and alliancing arrangements, which means that the overall responsibility of managing health and safety has to be shared. This may not be the case with a contract where the client may impose health and safety issues. The main body of outsourced contractors are agency workers, consultants and peripatetic or mobile workers, many of whom work from home. These individuals or organisations often do not have the benefit of in-house health and safety advice and rely to a degree on the client for appropriate support.

The use of contractors may lead to less supervision by people knowledgeable of the hazards of the plant; contractors may not have access to comprehensive health and safety advice or training; contractors may be under more stress because of the uncertainty of future work; commercial pressures or no corporate memory may be allowed to outweigh health and safety and, sometimes, the riskier work is outsourced. On the other hand, business re-organisation may lead to more efficient working and better health and safety management. Also, clients may be able to adopt good health and safety practice from specialist contractors.

Information available shows that the use of contractors has increased health and safety risks and that although accident rates are generally falling, they are higher for contractors' staff than direct employees. There is consensus that contractors have a greater exposure to risk and accident statistics tend to show that small firms have higher accident rates than large firms and many small firms work as contractors. However, it is not clear whether the higher rates are due to a small firm not having the same level of health and safety resources available to employees in larger firms or whether it is a result of working as a contractor.

Unsafe work practices damage both the client and contractor's reputation although the public will usually associate it with the client's site. Clients are well advised to ensure that their contractors have a good health and safety record and good practice is to have preferred contractor lists. A number of points emerge as good practice in the selection and use of contractors to ensure risks are properly controlled, ie:

- a risk assessment is carried out on the activity to be contracted out;

- a suitable contractor is selected;

- the contractor is given adequate information about the job, site-specific risks, rules and emergency arrangements the contractor understands what health and safety standards are expected;

- the client identifies the person to act on his behalf to liaise with the contractor, especially about any variations to the work proposed by the contractor;

- the arrangements for providing health and safety assurance are agreed between the client and contractor, including the level of supervision and control to be exercised by the client, monitoring to be carried out by the contractor, and reporting arrangements on health and safety matters;

- the effectiveness of the safety management arrangements are reviewed at intervals and after completion;

- there is agreement between client and contractor about the selection use and control of any sub-contractors;

- the client and contractor ensure there is co-operation and co-ordination between their employees and with any other contractor that the client has employed;

- the contractor advises the client of any risks that his work may cause to the clients employees or the public.

One of the crucial questions is what is the balance of responsibility between the client and contractor. In any client-contractor relationship both parties will always have some duties under health and safety legislation. A client cannot pass on all the responsibility to a contractor to ensure the work is carried out safely, but the extents of the responsibilities on each party will depend on the circumstances. Particular attention needs to be paid to situations where there are contractual chains to ensure that health and safety responsibilities are not blurred.

Clients' responsibilities

7.2 The factors, which increase the client's responsibilities are as follows:

- the client continues to work in the area and may affect the safety of contractor's staff;

- the client's undertaking has particular or peculiar risks, that the contractor may not be aware of;

- the client has specific rules and requirements for health and safety;

- the work being carried out by the contractor was previously done by the client's own employees;

- the work is frequently re-tendered and given to different contractors;

- the risk from the contractor's activities to the client's employees and/or the public is high;

- the degree of the client's health and safety knowledge and expertise;

- where the client appoints an employee to exercise some influence over the day to day running of the contract.

Contractors' responsibilities

7.3   The client cannot devolve any of its responsibilities, however, there are factors which increase the contractor's responsibilities when the client is not directly involved in the workplace activities and includes the following:

- the client has no work or permanent employees in the location of the work;

- there are no risks to the contractor's employees from the client's assets;

- the risks from the contractor's work are only to the contractor's employees;

- the work is specialist in nature and therefore the contractor has the greater knowledge and expertise; and where the client does not exercise any control over the contractor's design, arrangements or day-to-day running;

- whether different types of management arrangement, such as partnering or alliancing, affects health and safety culture and performance.

Also, whether corporate memory on health and safety issues is being eroded and how clients ensure they have sufficient staff with the right skills to manage contractors' work. This will extend where a contractor employs subcontractors to carry out some, or all, of the work, both the client and the main contractor retain some health and safety responsibilities.

Whenever a client contracts work the health and safety responsibilities of each party much be clear and good safety management systems need to be in place. Recent court cases have shown that the client will always retain some duties in respect of the health and safety of his employees, contractor's employees and the public.

The criminal law aspects of the relationship between contractors, subcontractors and employees in the context of health and safety legislation were considered in *Topek (Bur) Ltd v HM advocate (1998) SCCR 352.*

In this case, Topek installed a platform for a subcontractor. The company failed to instruct the subcontractor's employees in its use and also failed to ensure that work would be suspended in severe wind conditions. An employee of the subcontractor was killed when the platform overturned in high winds.

Topek Ltd was convicted under the HSWA 1974, s 3 for failing to ensure the health and safety of non-employees. The company was fined £20,000, which amounted to half of the company's profits, and although the company appealed against the penalty, it was dismissed. The court decided that it was an important feature of health and safety legislation that the principal contractor assumed responsibility for subcontractors and it was not appropriate for Topek to claim that it had relied on the subcontractor. The level of the fine had been assessed having taken into account Topek's profits and had not been arrived at arbitrarily.

Another case, which clearly shows that where contractors are concerned, responsibility for health and safety is a shared responsibility is that of *Associated Octel Company Ltd [1996] 1 WLR 1543 (HL)*. The company engaged an independent specialist contractor to repair the lining of a tank within their chemical plant. An employee of the contractor was badly burned when a broken light bulb ignited acetone vapor being used by the employee to clean the tank lining prior to repair. The contractor was convicted under section 2 of the HSWA 1974 and Octel were charged and convicted at the Crown Court for breach of section 3 of the Act.

Octel appealed to the Court of Appeal on the grounds that since a competent independent contractor did the work, they were conducting the undertaking and not Octel. Octel would only have a duty under the Act if they exercised control over the contractor's work. The Court of Appeal dismissed the case, stating that undertaking meant enterprise or business and that the cleaning, repair and maintenance of plant, machinery and buildings, necessary for carrying on business was part of the conduct of the undertaking whether or not such work was carried out by employees or by independent contractors. Octel appealed to the House of Lords.

The House of Lords affirmed the lower court's decision and dismissed the appeal. Whether a work activity is part of the conduct of an employer's undertaking, is a question of fact. It does not depend on whether the employer engages employees or independent contractors to carry out that work or whether control is exercised over the activity. If the work itself is part of the undertaking, a duty is owed under section 3 of the HSWA 1974 to ensure that it is done without risk - subject to *reasonable practicability*. The place where the activity takes place will, in the normal case, be an important determining factor.

Contractor management

7.4   The construction industry has not enjoyed a good safety record. To read the exploits of Isambard Kingdom Brunel immediately reveals a lack of safety leadership which nearly cost his own life. Brunel was a great engineer and his superbly designed railways, bridges and three great ships were more ambitious than anything attempted for decades after his death.

However, his drive and attitude to safety cost lives and, in 1828 while tunnelling under the Thames, it became apparent that debris from the river was pouring through the frames of the tunnel. Brunel kept his men at work, and while he was supervising work in the tunnel, disaster struck and the river burst through and flooded the workings. Brunel was found unconscious but survived. This is not a good example of leadership and, in general, his treatment of contractors was poor and on the Great Western Railway he left contractors bankrupt.

This great engineer pursued fame and put this before his desire to work safely. The European Union construction sector employs about 7% of the total workforce yet accounts for 30% of all fatalities in the industrial sector. This history of poor performance is compounded by the increasing numbers of self-employed and subcontract labour working on construction sites. As identified in the section on training in Chapter 10, a key requirement is to make the individuals appreciate the risk they are exposed to and the personal cost of failure. A survey conducted in 1991 revealed only about half the workforce thought their work posed a risk to their personal health and safety.

The need for further change in management and employee attitudes is recognised and has resulted in the Construction (Design and Management) Regulations 1994 (SI 1994/3140). These Regulations require specific planning to be undertaken prior to and during the construction phase and projects require safety plans before work starts on which tenders will have been based.

The plan drawn up by a nominated planning Supervisor will be passed to the selected principal contractor who has well-defined responsibilities for the control of the safety on site including other contractors. The plan becomes a working document through the duration of the project and will include risk assessments from all contractors. These will help, but ultimately the outcomes will be determined by the prime contractor's leadership and the behaviour all of site operatives.

Ultimately, the more powerful message is to undertake a one-to-one safety culture review with the MD of the proposed subcontractor. It is important to take time to visit his premises, find out what actions he personally takes to keep his staff safe, walk round his facilities and meet some of his staff and look at working standards. This sends a clear leadership message and displays commitment.

Principles of safety management

7.5   DuPont's principles of safety management (Dupont is discussed in Chapter 9) can be applied to any industry and are principles which should be adopted by a committed leader and which can be shared with subcontractors:

1.   All Injuries and occupational illnesses are preventable.

2.   Management is directly responsible for doing this with each level accountable to the one above and responsible for the level below.

3.   Safety is a condition of employment and is as important to the company as production quality or cost control.

4.   Training is required in order to sustain safety knowledge and includes establishing procedures and safety performance standards for each job.

5.   Safety audits and inspections must be carried out.

6.   Deficiencies must be corrected promptly by modifications, changing the procedures, improved training and/or consistent and constructive disciplining.

7.   All unsafe practices, incidents and injury accidents will be investigated.

8.   Safety away from work is as important as safety at work.

9.   Accident prevention is cost effective; the highest cost is human suffering.

People are the most critical element in the health and safety programme. Employees must be actively involved and complement management responsibility by making suggestions for improvement.

Contractors and subcontracting

7.6   To illustrate the amount of effort required by senior management to achieve a successful outcome, a project is highlighted where, despite demonstrable safety leadership and effort by both the client, a leading oil and gas operator, and the main contractor, there was still a failure resulting in a personal injury. All the contractors involved in the project were experienced long standing contractors and the contract with the client for all parties was reimbursable.

The fundamental requirements of pre-qualification were met and the operational and safety performance requirements clearly stated in bid documents. There are obvious legal requirements to state the safety rules to be followed and it is good practise to express the company's own safety expectations in the call for bid. Much attention was given to the competence of the nominated personnel to perform the workscope and, at supervisory level, their previous experience in working for the client and knowledge of their expectations was a consideration in the bid process. As part of the bidding process, a hazard and risk identification study was undertaken and a full risk assessment process was conducted after the contract award with representatives from all contractors.

In addition to these measures, meetings between the main contractor's senior management and the subcontractors' senior management were held to reinforce the safety expectations for the project and to reiterate that it was a reimbursable contract and there was not the pressure which can be associated with lump sum projects. The project would only be considered a success if it was completed without injury.

It was considered important to get this message across to the senior management of subcontractors as, historically, there have been many forms of contract used in the North Sea and the workforce must adopt to many styles of working. Although there was an overall initiative (The Step Change in Safety programme – a key industry initiative launched in September 1997 to improve health and safety performance, awareness and behaviours throughout the UK oil and gas industry) within the industry, there were cases where the workforce considered they were under pressure to perform and this could lead to unsafe acts.

It is obviously difficult for subcontractors to work safely and efficiently without clearly defined management lines, which extend back to the client who had established a well-resourced project team to manage the project, the main contractor and the subcontractor. The project mentioned above was to undertake underwater intervention work to re-establish the underwater integrity on one of the flexible risers between the subsea production system and the floating production storage and offtake vessel (FPSO) in the west of Shetland field. This required a dynamically positioned construction vessel equipped with remotely operated vehicles to undertake the underwater remedial work.

Safety first

7.7 The client stressed from the outset that the project would only be considered a success if there were no injuries to any of the workforce during the operation and that safety was the prime consideration. Several subcontractors were involved in the project, primarily fabricators to install temporary walkways on the deck of the construction support vessel. They were also required to fabricate steelwork platforms to mount the launching systems for the remotely operated vehicles that were going to be used to undertake the underwater workscope in the deep waters west of Shetland. The vessel for the project was chartered from the Finnish Maritime Association, which therefore acted as a prime subcontractor with the master responsible for the safety of all souls on board whilst at sea. A remotely operated vehicle and crew was also subcontracted in and were considered acceptable by the client in view of their previous extensive experience in the west of Shetland fields.

Even though the subcontractors were well known to the main contractor and had worked with them previously, in order to ensure their senior management fully understood the project safety expectations and both client and main contractor safety rules, personal visits were made to them by the senior management of the main contractor to ensure their complete engagement.

The client had nominated their own team to co-ordinate and supervise the works. In order to ensure all members of the work force were aware of the desire to complete the workscope without injury, it was agreed to hold a meeting with all the workforce while the vessel was in harbour and the equipment was being mobilised. To achieve this objective, it was also stressed that if any crew member saw or considered a situation or operation was not safe then they were entitled to stop the work. A presentation was made to the workforce by management representatives of the client, the main contractor and subcontractor's management, and the line supervisors and the vessel master were asked to reinforce the message.

The mobilisation of steelwork and equipment onto the vessel was then commenced. A temporary security office and a gangplank to the vessel was also established to control any personnel visiting the vessel on a short-term basis and to brief them on safety standards and expectations. One subcontracted remotely operated vehicle (ROV) operative arrived late on board and missed the detailed safety presentation. He was subsequently briefed by his line supervisor, where the focus of the briefing was centred on the requirement to wear full personal protective equipment on the back deck and not on the overall project safety objectives and the stop for safety message.

The ROV operative went on shift the morning after he arrived and the control van for his ROV operations had been secured on deck approximately 600 mm off the deck. Work was in progress to install temporary walkways and as he was keen to progress the hook-up of his control van, he climbed up into it. As steps had not been installed when he lowered himself onto the main deck of the vessel he stood on a small 20 mm stud that was protruding from the deck and cracked his ankle.

Despite the hazard identification process risk assessments, crew briefings and reinforcement of the stop for safety policy by management, a person had been injured. The remainder of the workscope, both onshore and offshore, which with a series of complex seabed operations, was completed without incident and the riser was repaired. However, as stated from the outset, the project was not considered successful due to the injury received by the ROV operator. Despite clear safety leadership efforts and management time there was a failure to convey the message that safety was the key priority and one of the crew suffered injury.

Best practice

7.8   An immediate investigation into the incident was launched and several other initiatives to drive home the message that safety was the prime consideration in conducting the work. It was decided to stop work programmes and hold discussions with smaller groups of workers rather than make further presentations to the entire crew. It was easier to relate to the smaller groups of operatives. Responses to the discussions were interesting and related to the perceived pressure to undertake the work in a timely manner despite the lack of any stated deadline to put the vessel to sea.

One of the comments from a marine fabricator was that they had been repairing vessels to a deadline all their working lives and the change to putting safety first was a new culture. Another fabricator stated the risk assessment process was new to their industry and their workforce would require further training. Many of the operatives only really appreciated the safety first message when it was communicated in the smaller groups. As a result of the feedback, a safety trainer was put onboard the vessel to reinforce the safety first message to the whole crew. An outcome of this incident and others that occurred in the industry during vessel mobilisations prompted the client to lead an industry task force with personnel from all the underwater construction companies to develop a best practise process for vessel mobilisations.

Management of contractors

7.9   The effective management of contractors on worksites is essential if high standards of safety are to be maintained. Fires on vessels at sea have often led to the total loss of the vessel with the obvious risks to the passengers and crew. During one safety visit to an offshore construction vessel, it was observed that a fire door in the corridor which accessed the main deck had been tied back when there was a sign on it saying it was to be normally closed. The chief engineer when questioned about this said he had grown tired of the door being wedged open by the crew and had finally decided to tie the door open. He realised this was not a safe action and when it was discussed during the safety visit immediately cut the rope but he stressed that the problem could arise again as the corridor was a main thoroughfare.

After liaison with the vessel authorities and a detailed risk assessment, an improved system was installed whereby the door was retained open with a magnetic catch which was released if the fire alarm was sounded.

Permits to work

7.10   Contractors working on a client's worksite who are undertaking critical workscopes can also be more effectively controlled under a 'permit to work' system. This requires a permit to be issued for the work and control measures are required as part of the process of issuing the permit.

Permits can be effective in improving safety but it is important to ensure the contractor has knowledge of the worksite. There remains a requirement for the client to have control over the operation and the contractor undertaking the work cannot be responsible for inspection of a worksite for which he may not have full details. Before a permit is issued, the client or the client's authorised representative must inspect the worksite.

An example of such a failure was observed on a vessel where some welding operations were being conducted on the main deck. A permit to work had been requested and authorised with control measures in place including a fire watch person who was located under the main deck to ensure no fires were started beneath deck as a result of heat being conducted through the deck. The work permit was authorised by a vessel officer on the bridge but the procedure was flawed and nobody from the vessel crew who had intimate knowledge of the vessel layout were required to visit the worksite. As a result of this and the welding contractor's lack of detailed knowledge of the vessel, the fire watch person was not stationed in the correct position beneath deck and did not observe the smoke that arose beneath deck as a result of the welding operation. Fortunately, another observant operator reported the smoke and no incident occurred.

The failure to control multiple contractors effectively can prove expensive as well as a safety risk. An example of this was observed on a vessel dry docking where the shipyard had been contracted to undertake a variety of modifications to a vessel and, as their own workforce was deployed on other projects, they had subcontracted many of the work scopes with a resultant lack of coordination. In one area of the vessel a burning operation was being conducted on the main deck. A fire watch and other precautions were in place but the sparks from the burning operation were falling onto switchgear, which had been opened up by another contractor to perform maintenance work with the obvious risk of damage to the switchgear. It is paramount that clients make available detailed information of a worksite to their contractors and that information must be effectively communicated to the workforce.

Commercial pressure on contractors

7.11   There is evidence that decisions which have a direct bearing on safety can be affected by commercial pressure. In the space shuttle *Challenger* disaster, which exploded as a result of failures in the solid rocket boosters, it was reported in the Presidential Commission's report that the day before the disaster the chief engineer of Thiokol, the contractor who provided the solid rocket boosters, attempted to stop the launch. The Thiokol management were concerned that NASA would no longer make them sole contractor for the boosters if the launch was held back and reversed the recommendation made by engineering.

The Presidential Commission report into the accident concluded that:

> 'that the Thiokol management reversed its position and recommended the launch at the urging of Marshall and contrary to the views of its engineers in order to accommodate a major customer'.

Furthermore, the commission found other flaws in decision-making and concluded that NASA appeared to be requiring a contractor to prove it was not safe to launch rather than proving it was safe.

The Port Ramsgate case

7.12   In 1995, six people were killed and seven others seriously injured when a ferry walkway at the Port of Ramsgate collapsed. This was not a manslaughter case, and the company was prosecuted under health and safety legislation. The outcome of the trial was a record fine of £1.7m. Two Swedish companies responsible for the design and construction of the walkway were fined £1m, Lloyd's Register of Shipping were fined £500,000 and Port Ramsgate Ltd were fined £200,000. Mr Justice Clarke determined that the companies had been guilty of gross negligence and that the level of fines were, in part, to deliver a message to directors of companies and the controlling minds of all organisations that the safety of the public is paramount. Port Ramsgate Ltd and the Swedish firms denied failing to ensure the safety of passengers, but were found guilty after a four-week trial. Lloyd's Register of Shipping, which issued a safety certificate, had pleaded guilty. The Swedish companies were tried and sentenced in their absence, not guilty pleas having been entered on their behalf. Fartygsentreprenader AB (FEAB) was fined £750,000 and

Fartygskonstruktioner AB (FKAB), who designed the walkway, was fined £250,000. In addition, costs of £251,000 were awarded jointly against these two companies. Lloyd's Register was fined £500,000 plus costs and Port Ramsgate Ltd were fined a total of £100,000. At the time of writing, the two Swedish companies have not paid either their fines or costs. This case raises the issue of liability with foreign companies operating in the UK who, it appears, can undertake work but not be liable for criminal offences. The HSE reiterated the view given in court that the project had been described as a shambles from beginning to end. The walkway, which should have lasted a lifetime, had been put into place in May and collapsed in September.

This is an interesting situation because the client Port Ramsgate had employed what they considered to be a competent contractor to undertake the work. The problem that follows is in a client making the judgement as to the competence of a contractor. Many contracts are put out to bid requiring evidence of past projects, any enforcement action or insurance claim action, either current or past. When the bids are received, the accountants step in and look at the lowest figure. It may well be that the financial benefits will overcome any review of health and safety issues. An added problem that arose in this case was that the company that was engaged to review the safety status had issued certificates. Many would ask what more could a client do to ensure remaining within the law.

In practice, there needs to be a detailed audit of potential contractors. It needs to be determined if any of the work is in turn subcontracted and, if it is, then that undertaking needs to be audited. The audit can be undertaken by in-house personnel if they have the required expertise, otherwise, a third party or specialists can be used. Whilst the financial implications have a bearing in the selection process, it should be part of the overall package of contractor selection to include competence to undertake the work, the identification as to who would undertake the actual work and the financial aspects.

Fine-dodge loophole blocked

7.13   Euro MPs have backed plans to block legal loopholes that currently allow companies to escape payment of fines imposed in Britain. If approved by EU governments, tighter laws will force firms in other EU countries to meet their financial obligations.

In cases such as the Ramsgate walkway disaster, when six people died, and the Heathrow tunnel collapse, European companies had been found liable and ordered by British judges to pay hefty fines. But so far, they had failed to do so. At present, such fines are not enforceable across the EU.

However, that position could now change after MEPs voted in favour of the 'mutual recognition' of fines across all 15 EU member states. Labour health and safety spokesman, Peter Skinner MEP, stated:

> 'For too long, legal loopholes have allowed companies to dodge fines imposed by British courts. Without co-operation between EU member states, we have gaping holes, which allow big companies to run rings around the law.

> If companies are sure that their products are safe, they must be prepared to take full financial responsibility for them. We cannot bring back those who died at Port Ramsgate, but we can tighten the law to enforce tough penalties. By stepping up EU co-operation, we are sending a strong signal that companies who do not respect health and safety regulations will face the full force of the law'.

It is very evident that undertakings who engage contractors and subcontractors do not relinquish their obligations with regard to health and safety. Good management in the selection and control of activities will ensure co-operation by all of those involved.

Chapter 8

Practical Risk Management

Introduction

8.0   This chapter considers the practical steps that can be taken to develop a safety management system which will help to protect a company's assets and people. The need for a safety management system has been explored and now it is a case of adapting the process in a practical way to suit the specific needs of an undertaking. There is no fixed solution as the process is flexible and from the examples shown, any undertaking can have effective procedures.

Personal risk management

8.1   Often when interviewing an injured party after an incident there is a sudden realisation from the individual that the accident that he or she never thought would happen has – and that person pays the price both in human and financial terms. More often than not, it is enthusiasm and a desire to progress their workscope that results in injury, such as when short cuts are taken and working processes are not adopted.

On one occasion, an offshore technician was moving fast across the back deck of a construction support vessel. The vessel's deck was wet and the technician slipped injuring his ankle. In another incident, a technician was working inside a diving bell and lying in an awkward position to open the steel bottom door. He succeeded in opening the door but did not secure it in the open position and it closed on his leg and injured it.

In both cases there was an instant realisation: first, a simple realisation that it was difficult to travel with such injuries, and second, how they could explain to their wives what had happened. Both were extremely responsible hard-working individuals who also realised they had jeopardised their ability to earn money and fend for their families. Incidents such as these result from enthusiasm and the injured parties receive support from fellow colleagues and management.

Breach of safety rules

8.2   Incidents which do not receive sympathy are where safety rules are clearly broken and unsafe acts committed. In one incident, a life support technician had left a diving support vessel to visit the shops near the harbour. During his trip the diving support vessel had to change berths and when the technician returned, the vessel was still being moored up and the gangway was being re-established and secured. The technician was impatient and asked if he could get back onboard before the gangway was secured. Both the vessel's captain and a diving supervisor instructed him to wait until the gangway was secured. However, the technician decided to jump onto the back deck of the vessel and broke his leg when he landed. He received little immediate sympathy from the crew and, after a detailed investigation and consultation with the vessel's management team, the technician was dismissed for gross misconduct.

The type of behaviour where safety rules are deliberately broken cannot be condoned by a safety leader. It is difficult to understand why people behave like this and put themselves at risk and it is possible they do not consider they will injure themselves and certainly they rarely appear to consider the effects of an injury.

Personal experience

8.3   It can be frustrating to attend safety training courses and see the lack of interest; even when the lecturer is passionate about his subject and tries hard to engage the audience. It is essential for all employees to understand that the basis of safety management is to protect a company's prime asset – its employees. However, to gain employees' attention and instil an appreciation that accidents can and do happen, a more graphic illustration (as discussed below) of the results of unsafe acts and lacking safety management systems can have more impact.

One such presentation was given to a hushed audience, the presenter had been blinded in an industrial accident when mixing two chemicals together and they exploded in his face. He has since dedicated the rest of his life to helping others understand the terrible cost of accidents (see **8.8** below). Simply by wearing safety glasses he would have mitigated his eye injuries but the accident nearly cost him his life had it not been for the intervention of a fellow worker who pulled him into a shower. The impact on the hushed audience was obvious during the presentation and afterwards many people commented on the power of the presentation.

That presentation was given from someone in the onshore food and drink industry and an even more powerful message was given to people in the offshore industry from a construction manager. The construction manger admitted he had been progressing a project too rapidly and paid the price personally. He walked out on deck to look at some deck mounted pipeline installation equipment but there was a failure in the equipment which resulted in his neck being broken. He did not discuss the accident in detail, but spoke of the trauma of the operations and pain he endured as a result of the accident. He was also an extremely active sportsman prior to his accident and can no longer pursue the sports he enjoyed. This was a very powerful message to the offshore workforce, who are generally a robust group and who may consider themselves 'unbreakable'.

Offshore incidents

8.4   Regrettably, the enthusiasm to progress work can result in fatalities and two offshore accidents bear testimony to this. In both cases, loads were being lifted onto rigs and were being stacked on other equipment. In the first incident the load had been temporarily landed and one of the banksmen placed himself close to the load to observe how it had landed, the load slipped and he was crushed against another piece of steelwork. On the evening prior to this incident the operator had stressed to the crew that their safety was the top priority.

A short while later, another fatality occurred when a chemical container was being stacked on another container, again the crewman tried to clear the lift line, the container slipped and crushed him. The operator is obviously reviewing its processes for stacking loads on offshore installations and a shocking message may be necessary to prevent further incidents such as these.

Much of this appears to come down to human behaviour and it is interesting to see parallels with regard to personal protective safety equipment. For example, in a Brazilian operation, it had proved difficult to get some of the offshore crews to wear protective eyewear on the back decks of vessels. This was originally put down to the discomfort in the high temperatures, however, when stylish, tinted safety glasses were sourced, the problem rapidly diminished. It is, therefore, worth sourcing comfortable personal equipment if companies want employees to readily comply with their standards.

Safety standards outside the UK

8.5   Safety legislation around the world may vary considerably and it is an obvious test of leadership to develop common standards wherever one is working. For example, when travelling offshore in a helicopter in the UK North Sea, very strict safety standards are followed. A basic requirement is for the traveller to have undertaken an offshore survival course which goes through the basics of what to do in the event an emergency ditching of a helicopter offshore and includes practical work on how to get into life rafts and includes a simulated dunking where a helicopter has made an emergency landing on water and then rolls over in the water. The trainee is instructed to locate an emergency exit with one hand and hold the seatbelt release with the other because it can be disorientating as the helicopter simulator rolls over in the water. Once the helicopter has ceased moving and is upside down is it possible to make an escape.

This type of exercise helps to build confidence when travelling offshore and the provision of personal safety equipment gives a degree of comfort. A survival suit is provided to help against hypothermia in the event of immersion in the sea and, more recently, personal locator beacons have been introduced by some operators and also a rebreather device which, in the event of a helicopter inverting on the water surface, would give the occupants a better opportunity to exit the helicopter by allowing them to breath underwater through the rebreather.

Offshore, the helicopter landing decks are well controlled by trained helicopter landing officers and strict rules are observed to minimise the risk to passengers when refuelling the helicopters. Prior to making a helicopter journey offshore in the UK there is also a full safety briefing specific to that particular helicopter and all emergency procedures for the passengers are demonstrated.

Example of other safety standards

8.6   During a safety audit in the Gulf of Mexico, senior management decided to demonstrate leadership and fly offshore to visit one of their offshore construction vessels. A helicopter was chartered and, when checking in for their flight, they naturally expected a safety briefing from the staff. There was, however, no briefing and the pilot only asked if they had flown in a helicopter before.

The vessel was some 90 kms offshore and the chartered helicopter only had a single engine and one pilot. In the North Sea it has been accepted practice for the past 25 years to have a pilot and co-pilot on offshore flights. In fact, in this instance, a co-pilot would have had little ability to assist in the flying of the helicopter as it did not have dual controls. There were no ground crew on hand and the pilot just started the helicopter and took off. The pilot did not have an autopilot system nor were there personal locator devices or re-breather sets for the passengers. The whole operation would give little confidence to anyone familiar with travelling offshore in the North Sea.

En route to the vessel, the back passenger door of the helicopter came open, which required some effort to close the door in flight; the door by the co-pilot's seat also came open and had to be slammed shut again. During the landing on the vessel, the helicopter landing officer endangered himself by walking in an area where the rotor blades could have caused him serious injury. As a result, he was subsequently coached on the need to stay clear of the rotor blades, particularly in view of the smaller helicopters utilised in the Gulf of Mexico.

For the return flight, the helicopter was equipped two engines, which gave a degree of confidence, and the flight was scheduled to take around an hour. After about 45 minutes into the flight, the helicopter moved close to a line of black storm clouds and every time the helicopter went near them it was buffeted around. The pilot turned the helicopter and flew along the bank of cloud whilst looking down at the markings of the helicopter landing decks on the platforms below. He appeared to be having problems with the hand-held Global Positioning System navigation unit he was utilising. The flight had now taken far longer than planned and, with no warning to the passengers, the pilot flew the helicopter to an offshore platform and landed on it.

In the North Sea a trained firefighter is normally in attendance when landing and refuelling, however, there was nobody on this particular helicopter landing area. Eventually, a platform operative came onto the deck, pulled out a fuelling hose and proceeded to refuel the helicopter with the engines running and passengers onboard. There were no firefighters with equipment. When the helicopter was refuelled, the platform operative left the helicopter deck and returned with some batteries. It transpired that the pilot was having problems navigating. He was not using the helicopter's navigation system but was flying using a hand held unit, unfortunately, the batteries had expired. After the refuelling, the helicopter took off again to continue the journey.

The following day, enquiries were made to staff for their views on the helicopter flights and an engineer commented that the incident experienced the previous day was not unusual, as a passenger on one flight, he had actually got off to help with the refuelling of the helicopter.

A complaint was made to the helicopter company with the hope that a full review of their operational processes would be carried out to ensure that such incidents did not repeat themselves. However, the helicopter company's management dismissed the pilot, which was not the outcome that had been sought. Concerned that the company was not managing the situation, a helicopter expert was brought in to audit all of the helicopter companies used to ensure that they were operating to safe standards. The helicopter company involved in the incidents described above carried out its own detailed investigations and issued a series of safety improvement notices. An outcome from this audit stated that the helicopter company had one of the best safety records of all its competitors.

In the months following these eventful flights, there were two helicopter incidents involving fatalities in the Gulf of Mexico: one where a passenger was involved in refuelling operations and another where a single-engine helicopter was forced to ditch. All of which confirms the leadership message that lessons must be learned from mistakes which, in this case, unfortunately, did not happen.

It was obvious that for global standards to be raised to those of the UK North Sea industry then more effort would be required. In a situation such as this where standards in a sector of an industry appear inferior to those experienced elsewhere in the world, then a trade association can assist in the drive to improve standards globally. In this case, a request was made to the representative body for offshore contractors, the International Marine Contractors Association, who had a track record in promoting global safety standards.

Training and development

8.7   The prime factor in driving a positive safety culture in an entity is to have a leader in place who is passionate with regard to the safety of his employees and the business integrity of the entity. This provides a firm foundation for success but, as with any team, the leader will ultimately rely on his 'players' and these people will need to be trained and understand the benefits of a safe company in relation to their employment prospects, the safety objectives and safety systems, and the legal framework within which companies operate.

The question is often asked how, with today's diverse multi-national workforce, can safety be managed when many workers come from areas of the world where safety is not high on the corporate agenda? One of the solutions has to be with safety training that makes an impact on the employees and this has to be the dramatic effect accidents can have on their ability to earn a living and provide for their families. Unfortunately, safety training is not a subject which many employees enthuse over. It is often frustrating to watch younger employees and their attitude toward training; this could be because when younger they consider themselves bomb proof and cannot be hurt through industrial accidents.

Effective safety leaders have often been closely involved in an incident or accident and witnessed first hand the misery which can be caused through an industrial injury and they endeavour to limit the disastrous effects of an employee fatality. This can dramatically change a manager's attitude regarding his responsibility for the safety of employees or subcontractors.

Learning from mistakes of others

8.8   As part of an effective training programme, consideration should be given to utilising the services of a trainer who has suffered from an industrial injury. Such a trainer is Ken Woodward who was blinded in an industrial accident. He is now committed to improving industrial safety by presenting his story to industry. It is a compelling and very personal story is very effective in gaining the complete attention of his audience. There are some extremely powerful messages in Ken's presentation but he acknowledges one of his workmates for saving him from more extensive injury. His fellow worker was working one day and noticed an eye wash shower had been damaged. There did not appear to be a positive safety culture in the company and the employee took it upon himself to go into work over a weekend and repair the shower unit, it was this shower which mitigated Ken's injuries when he was mixing chemicals and they blew up in his face. (There are, however, more issues to this incident than just the shower; Ken had no training, it was the third incident in a row and the second was still under investigation and there was severe production pressure.)

The presentations on legislation and the management of risk as described in this book are beneficial, but to have a real impact on both employees and management, first-hand experience to the effects of safety failure have the most significant impact.

Behavioural training is another important component of a training agenda. Employees generally know what they have to do but sometimes do not do it. An effective workshop involving employees in detailed discussion about what really affects people can help them reveal why they occasionally work unsafely and safety experts can help them address these pressures and work more safely.

Outline Training Programme

8.9   An outline of an effective safety training programme is reproduced in **Appendix A** at the end of this book. Much of the success or failure of any training programme will depend on the trainer who should also have a passion for the subject because safety is generally not perceived as a prime business driver when considered against production, costs and profitability.

Management of change

8.10   The effective management of change is an essential process in today's fast-moving business environment, change can affect many aspects of a business and uncontrolled change can be detrimental to safety performance. There have been several major disasters where lack of control over management of change has been a significant contributory factor in the incidents. One such incident was the Flixborough (Nypro UK) explosion in June 1974.

Flixborough – accident summary

8.11   On Saturday, 1 June 1974, the Nypro (UK) site at Flixborough (near Scunthorpe) was severely damaged by a large explosion. 28 workers were killed and a further 30 suffered injuries. The number of casualties could have been greater if the incident had occurred on a weekday. Offsite 53 people were injured.

Prior to the explosion in March 1974 it was discovered that a vertical crack in reactor No 5 was leaking cyclohexane. The plant was subsequently shut down for an investigation. This identified a serious problem with the reactor and the decision was taken to remove it and install a bypass assembly to connect reactors No 4 and No 6 so the plant could continue production. During the afternoon of 1 June 1974, a 20-inch bypass system ruptured, which may have been caused by fire on a nearby 8-inch pipe. This resulted in the escape of cyclohexane. The cyclohexane formed a flammable mixture and subsequently found a source of ignition. At about 16.53 hrs there was a massive vapour cloud explosion which caused extensive damage and started numerous fires on the site. 18 fatalities occurred in the control room as a result of the windows shattering and the collapse of the roof. No one escaped from the control room.

A finding of the inquiry was that a plant modification occurred without a full assessment of the potential consequences. Only limited calculations were undertaken on the integrity of the bypass line. No calculations were undertaken for the dog-legged shaped line or for the bellows and no drawing of the proposed modification was produced and no pressure testing was carried out on the installed pipework modification.

➢   **Help Point:** The HSE's publication, 'Flixborough Disaster: Report of the Court of Inquiry' HMSO, ISBN 0113610750, 1975.

Bhopal – accident summary

8.12   Around ten years after the Flixborough incident, a far greater disaster in terms of human suffering occurred in 1984 when approximately 2,000 people died and tens of thousands were injured when a release of toxic gas occurred. It was Union Carbide India Ltd, Bhopal, India.

In the early hours of 3 December 1984, a relief valve on a storage tank containing highly toxic methyl isocyanate lifted. A cloud of methyl isocyanate was released which drifted onto nearby housing.

The day before, an operator noticed the pressure inside the storage tank to be higher than normal but not outside the working pressure of the tank. At the same time, a methyl isocyanate leak was reported near the vent gas scrubber. At 00.15 hrs a methyl isocyanate release in the process area was reported. The pressure in the storage tank was rising rapidly so the operator went outside to the tank. Rumbling sounds were heard from the tank and a screeching noise from the safety valve. Radiated heat could also be felt from the tank. Attempts were made to switch on the vent gas scrubber but this was not operational.

The severity of this accident makes it the worst recorded in the chemical industry. Several technical failings were identified but lack of control of change management was identified as follows.

The flare system was a critical element within the plant's protection system. However, this fact was not recognised as it was out of commission for some three months prior to the accident.

The ingress of water caused an exothermic reaction with the process fluid. The exact point of ingress is uncertain though poor modification/ maintenance practises may have contributed.

The decommissioning of the refrigeration system was one plant modification that contributed to the accident. Without the system, the temperature in the tank was higher than the design temperature of zero degrees centigrade.

➢ **Help Point:** Lees FP, *Loss prevention in the process industries- Hazard identification, assessment and control* (Vol 3, App 5, Butterworth Heinemann (1996) ISBN 0 7506 1574 8.

Examples of failure to manage change

8.13 Both of the examples referenced where failure to manage change effectively has led to extensive loss of life are from the chemical industry. Change need not only refer to design changes in equipment and uncontrolled modifications, but can apply when senior management changes are made or during downsizing or when work is subcontracted out, such as occurred when much of the maintenance work previously carried out with internal resources was contracted out in the railway industry.

The need to manage change effectively, therefore, is a requirement in a wide range of industries and examples of failures can be observed in a variety of industries.

In the subsea construction industry, two incidents are described below which could have resulted in loss of life. For underwater lifting operations inflatable lift bags are often utilised which rely on the Archimedes' principle that upthrust equals the weight of fluid displaced. These lift bags are often utilised at the seabed to lift equipment and are efficient with the advantage that by avoiding the use of a lift line deployed from a surface support vessel, the load can be decoupled from the effect of the vessel motions. A disadvantage with lift bags results from the fact that, as the lift bag rises, the air in the lift bag expands and displaces more fluid resulting in a greater capacity to lift. It is, therefore, possible to lose control of lifts and load being lifted must be accurately known.

During a subsea lifting operation to remove a valve from a manifold a lift bag was sized to give the correct lift, regrettably during the manufacture of the manifold the weight of the valve was changed and not recorded. This resulted in the valve and lift bag taking off from the seabed and accelerate to the water surface. At the surface, the air in the lift bag was lost and the valve and lift bag then made an uncontrolled descent back to the seabed with the obvious risk to the diver working at the manifold. In this incident no injury was sustained, it was recorded as a near miss and lessons were learnt and procedures modified.

It is essential when using a diving bell to carry divers to the seabed that there is control of the pressure in the bell as the divers have gas under pressure in their blood stream and they have to be decompressed slowly under controlled conditions. This process will be over a period of days allowing the gas to slowly release from their blood stream. In one tragic case where a diving bell became unmated from the surface chamber, the pressure in the system was lost rapidly and all the divers in the system were killed due to the rapid decompression.

Another alarming incident in a diving bell came about as a result of an uncontrolled change to the plumbing of pipework and control valves that carry the breathing gas from the surface to bell. In a maintenance programme, a bell internal valve position was moved and during a subsequent diving operation one of the divers inadvertently opened the valve whilst moving about. He was unfamiliar with the new position of the valve and his ability to find the valve to close it was made difficult because of the mist that formed in the bell environment as a result of the decompression process. The increasing concern of the diving supervisor and the unsuccessful attempts of the divers in the bell to shut the valve were clearly recorded on the audio visual system Fortunately, the diving bell had been recovered from the seabed and was on the surface and a support operative was able to stop the loss of pressure by closing the external valve on the line. If the rapid decompression had not been stopped the incident could have resulted in fatalities.

Good practice

8.14 The Chemical Industries Association Safety Advisory Group outlines the following good practice related to plant modification/change procedures.

- Members of staff must be aware of the hazards associated with the work they carry out and be able to determine that the risks involved are acceptable.

- Risk assessment must be carried out to determine the possibility and consequence of the hazards being realised. If necessary, appropriate precautions must be taken to minimise the risk.

- All modifications, whether involving procedures, plant and equipment, people or substances, should be subject to formal management procedures. The procedure should draw reference to:

  (a) evidence from previous incidents – their cause and means of preventing them;

  (b) the intrinsic link between process definition and the validity of the hazard evaluation;

  (c) the options that are available in the design of safety measures;

  (d) preventative measures (process control, instrumentation etc.);

  (e) protective measures (containment, reactor venting, quenching, reaction inhibition).

Good industry practice requires that process and plant modifications should not be undertaken without having undertaken a safety, engineering and technical review. This review should be traceable and identify changes proposed to the following factors, process conditions, operating methods, engineering methods, safety, environmental conditions and engineering hardware and design. A form of risk assessment should then identify what hazards have been created by the change that may affect plant or personnel safety, and what action can be implemented to reduce or eliminate the risk.

Additional hazards that may be introduced which need to be considered are fire, explosion and loss of containment. Changes may affect other parts of the plant which may be quite remote from the source of the change. Therefore, all parts of the plant should be considered in undertaking hazard identification and risk assessments.

Factors that are crucial to the success and safe implementation of a plant modification procedure include corporate history, communication between different departments, recognition of authorised personnel and accurate recording and monitoring of changes to plant and process.

Change control process

8.15 An example of a change control process is illustrated in **Appendix B**. The flowchart shown in the Appendix is the work of Phil Bradbury of Integrated Subsea Services and forms part of their safety management system. The flowchart describes the processes which are required to be adopted in Safety Management Systems. Such systems are invaluable in providing safe systems of work on a step-by-step basis for any project. In this case it is based on an offshore diving operation.

Incident and near miss reporting

8.16 The most challenging role in achieving excellence in safety performance is to predict future undesirable events and mitigate against them before they occur. Achieving success in this objective results in non-events and it takes self-discipline to maintain the effort.

It is relatively easy to measure lagging indicators of safety performance and to respond to actual accidents with improvements but proactive preventative action will improve safety performance. The requirement for near miss or high potential incident reporting is essential in a business where there is a desire for a positive safety culture. There are, unfortunately, many examples where fatalities have occurred which could have been prevented had the warning signals been heeded and management showed leadership.

The Herald of Free Enterprise

8.17 In the *Herald of Free Enterprise* ferry disaster there was no information display (not even a single warning light) to tell the captain if the bow doors were open. Two years earlier, the captain of a similar vessel owned by the same company had requested that a warning light should be installed following a similar incident when he had gone to sea with his bow doors open. Company management had treated the request with derision. Following the loss of the *Herald of Free Enterprise*, bow door lights were made mandatory on roll-on roll-off car ferries.

➤ **Help Point:** Source: the 'SafetyLine' information service can be found at www.safetyline.wa.gov.au/institute

The Challenger

8.18 The Commission which investigated the space shuttle *Challenger* disaster which, on 28 January 1986, disintegrated seconds after the launch killing all seven people onboard, concluded that the accident was due to the failure in the pressure seal in the aft field joint of the right solid rocket booster. A contributing cause of the accident was determined to be the flawed decision to launch. The Commission concluded that there was a serious flaw in the decision-making process leading up to the flight. A well-structured and managed system emphasising safety would have flagged the rising doubts about the solid rocket booster joint seal.

➢ **Help Point:** Source: The Presidential Commission on the Space Shuttle Challenger Accident Report, 6 June 1986.

Ladbroke Grove

8.19 On 5 October 1999, a train passed a red signal at Ladbroke Grove and continued on for some 700 metres into the path of a high-speed train. As a result of the collision and the subsequent fires, 31 people died and 227 were taken to hospital.

There were several incidents where drivers had crossed this signal (SN 109) at red and it was reported at the inquiry that following the seventh and eighth time the signal was passed at danger (SPAD), David Franks, the Production Director of Thames Trains, informed the inquiry that as both SPADs had involved experienced drivers and that:

> 'in view of the failure to carry out remedial action I insisted that Railtrack should accept that the primary cause of these SPADs was the signalling equipment itself. I accepted the drivers had some responsibility but this was not the root cause'.

In his report on the Ladbroke Grove Rail Inquiry, Part 2, Lord Cullen stated in the summary at 1.15:

> 'The evidence clearly demonstrated that the rail industry needs to develop the ability to behave as a learning organisation. I identify a number of areas of importance. First, identifying unsafe acts and conditions and taking prompt steps to deal with them. Secondly, applying and disseminating the lessons of accidents and incidents (including near misses). Here the evidence showed the process was inhibited by the 'blame culture', and the lack of a co-ordinated system for the collation of recommendations and ensuring that they were followed up. Thirdly, using risk assessment in order to drive improvements in safety. Fourthly, gaining benefit from the process of auditing. This has been less than fully effective. Fifthly, using data and analytical tools. The evidence shows there were weaknesses in the industry's use of these materials. Sixthly, training with particular reference to refresher courses, into which greater effort requires to be put'.

At 1.16 he stated:

> 'Finally I direct attention to the desirability of the industry developing a culture in which there is a progressive movement from a situation where management make the rules and tell employees what to do, to a situation

where individuals can contribute ideas and effort, while complying with the rules and procedures, through to a position where there is a committed, dedicated team approach, with a high degree of interdependency between teams and across company boundaries'.

All of the disasters referred to above had warning signs that were either ignored or not given full management attention.

> **Help Point:** 'The Ladbroke Grove Rail Inquiry' Part 2. Executive Summary by the Right Hon Lord Cullen PC (available at www.hse.gov.uk/railways/paddrail/lgri2.pdf).

Databases

8.20 There are now effective databases available for any type of undertaking to enter data and monitor that actions have been completed regarding all safety incidents and near misses. Remote worksites are able to input their incident details directly into the database so there is an immediate degree of ownership and the systems have the capability to alert all worksites to any accident or high potential near miss. Local management teams can be formed to close out their own incidents and implement improvements, and on a regular basis, senior management can review the incidents and confirm their approval of the improvement measures taken. For a large company, software can also group incidents and near misses to assist senior management to analyse trends with high potential near misses. A team from senior management with operational and engineering skills can be established to monitor trends and, having recognised a trend, may request line management to issue a series of measures to mitigate against further incidents.

This system can work for any type of business and industry, an example of this is where an analysis of near miss reports identified that there had been several instances of small fires in a vessel fleet. It showed that each incident must be fully investigated but the issue can be raised with all vessel masters reminding them of the basic requirements of fuel, heat and oxygen required to create a fire situation. Many vessel fires come about as a result of poor housekeeping and a heightened awareness of housekeeping might be requested. On vessel visits attention should be paid to fire doors and it should be confirmed that fire doors are maintained closed if they are required to be closed to slow the spread of a fire.

A simple discussion between a vessel master and a senior manager regarding the issue of fires on vessels will demonstrate a concern and can result in a heightened awareness of the issue of fire. A visit to the engine room and a discussion with the chief engineer and a request to view the exhaust insulation in a vessel and the protection of fuel oil lines from heat sources will raise the profile further. A request from management for a review and report of obvious sources of fires on a vessel is a proactive measure which will raise the profile of the issue – the galley, laundry and hot work permitting systems are obvious areas for review. Regular safety audits should be undertaken with a focus on fire prevention and all actions resulting from the audits should be closed out. Where large numbers of subcontractors are involved in a dry docking, it may be necessary to employ additional safety officers to ensure permitting systems and fire watches are effective and this is an obvious and visible demonstration that management is committed to the safety agenda.

All of the above measures will demonstrate a positive culture and are practical measures to mitigate against further incidents. If it is considered that there is an industry issue as a result of accidents and high potential near misses, such as has been determined in the offshore industry with lifting operations, benefit can be gained from refresher training in the need for risk assessments and consideration given to a basic risk assessment being undertaken on all lifts.

There are reasonable practical solutions to all of the recommendations raised in Lord Cullen's observations quoted at **8.18** above, which, if implemented, will drive a positive safety culture and safety performance.

Safety audits

8.21 There is a proven need for undertakings to audit their activities and gain from the benefits derived from effective safety audits. The audit process is adaptable for all undertakings and, in this example, the high risk offshore industry is focused upon to provide an example. Prior to the *Piper Alpha* disaster, HSE inspectors would regularly visit offshore worksites and the focus of the visits were primarily to inspect equipment for compliance with standards and legal requirements. Operators and contractors could use these inspections as audits and it effectively reduced their responsibility to ensure by self-audit that they had safe systems of work. A clean bill of health from the HSE could give rise to a false sense of security for operators and contractors.

The Cullen Inquiry recommendations changed this prescriptive regime into a more self-regulating regime and the HSE inspectors began to review safety management systems and arrangements determined under the safety cases the operators were required to put in place for their facilities. Inspectors would also more actively seek the opinions of the offshore workforce to confirm safety was a priority for their employers. The main guidance on the requirement to audit is documented in the Health and Safety at Work Regulations 1999 which defines auditing as:

'The structured process of collecting independent information on the efficiency effectiveness and reliability of the total health and safety management system and drawing up plans for corrective action'.

The audit process must, therefore, be conducted to confirm the arrangements that are in place to assure the safety of employees, contractors, the public and other parties that may be affected by an operation's activities and products. The principal elements of a safety management system must be confirmed by the audit process. This will include a review of:

- leadership and commitment;

- policy and strategic objectives;

- organisation, responsibilities resources, standards and documents;

- hazard and effects management;

- planning and procedures;

- implementation and monitoring;

- audit;

- management review.

Over the course of their careers, the authors have had extensive experience of both auditing and being subjected to audits. It is considered that one of the most effective safety audits observed was conducted by a major oil operator by a team of auditors of various technical backgrounds, which initially involved a paper review of all policies, standards, processes and procedures and then a series on interviews.

The audit team drew up an extensive series of interview questions. They commenced with interviews of the most senior management and then conducted interviews down the management chain right through to the operatives on the back deck of the offshore vessels in order to confirm the management safety messages and systems were well communicated and effective and that the safety of employees had the same status in the company as the desire to make a profit. To be effective, agreed audit actions must be drawn up and improvements implemented. Audits by third parties should be considered as a learning opportunity and should be welcomed by progressive companies. An effective internal audit programme is also essential to ensure systems are effective.

Audit interview questions

8.22   Examples of possible audit interview questions for the president or managing director of an offshore contractor are illustrated in **Appendix C**

at the back of this book. In context, these questions are also applicable to any undertaking.

Behavioural change – human factors

8.23   Behavioural change or human factors are an integral part of the leadership management process and the authors are indebted to specialist input by Tim Southam. He was an RAF Pilot on Jaguar (Recce) and Tornado aircraft. Following his service he managed human factors research projects at Farnborough, including human workload, spatial awareness and cognitive information processing. His main interest has focused on the way people interact in the workplace and the differing perceptions that reduce or prevent people communicating in an open and unobtrusive way. He has focused on developing and integrating behavioural techniques directly into management systems. These techniques require strong system analysis skills that enable the reduction and the drain on people to make the whole organisation more responsive to change.

Improvements in safety, health and environmental performance and the subsequent reduction in injuries have historically been achieved through improvements in engineering and enhanced safety management systems. However, in future, performance gains will only be achieved by understanding the way people interact within every aspect of the workplace through the full integration and understanding of human factors principles. This will also lead to optimum utilisation of human performance, enhanced reliability, greater efficiency, greater margins and lower costs.

Human factors covers all aspects of design and operations such as:

- workplace design in terms of operability, man machine interface;

- plant design, manually handling large or heavy loads;

- personal protective equipment in terms of fit for purpose and working environment; and

- job design in terms of 'can we achieve what is expected of us'.

Indeed the HSE's guidance, HSG48, clearly identifies the realm of human factors and defines the subject as:

> 'Human factors refers to environmental, organisational and job factors, and human and individual characteristics which influence behaviour at work in a way which can affect health and safety'.

Most people can relate to human factors being referred to as 'applied common sense' and, in the same breath, one has to ask why is it therefore so often forgotten? There can be many answers for this, and perhaps it is because it is considered to be 'common sense' that it is so often overlooked. Human factors or ergonomics is far-reaching and not limited to the design of door handles and workstations but every aspect of managing the human element of risk. One can see that it will therefore play a part in nearly all hardware and software systems, human interaction, equipment and plant, procedures and working environment design. Sometimes this triad is referred to as hardware, software and liveware but the analogy of a three-legged stool is very valid within the context of safety management.

So why is human factors so often forgotten?

8.24   Some of the real reasons behind the lack of inclusion of human factors into the main stream thinking could include:

- designers are engineers and do not fully understand how people have to interact with their equipment throughout the product lifecycle;

- people simply do not understand what is required;

- perception will cost money and time;

- it raises 'difficult' and awkward questions.

This is not meant to be a damning statement about designers, as it is believed that the vast majority of personnel involved in this process do want to produce good safe designs. It is a statement that there is still a long way to go to have human factors accepted as a fundamental element of the design process. The benefits of including human factors into the design, should generally be common sense, however, they include;

- real safety improvements built into the design;

- demonstration of the considerations;

- highlight the human factors elements within the safety case;

- create a positive human factors image within the project.

Now we have identified all the good reasons, the question follows, what does it take to put it into practice?

- project commitment – a genuine passion and desire;

- a dedicated project resource;

- education at all levels, within, and external to, the project;

- design and operations input;

- perseverance.

This is not as simple as it sounds as there are a number of stages which have to be tied into. Education plays a major part and it was found quite quickly that it was very necessary in order to ensure project awareness of human factors as described in HSG48. It is also very difficult to bring the elements of human factors into a project until a design is on the table.

Future performance gains

8.25 Future performance gains will only be achieved by taking more account of the way people interact with every aspect of the workplace, sometimes called culture, through the integration and understanding of the human factors principles into a risk management methodology.

In a genuine search for the 'best practice' it is identified that a process that integrates all the human factors methodologies into the core management system of the business. Undertaking a climate survey will highlight where work needs to be done or where difficulties are perceived to be in the business is often the first step to understanding the impact of change.

Human factors has been recognised by the HSE who have published their 'Top Ten Human Factors Issues'. They are:

1. organisational change;

2. de-manning and staffing levels;

3. training and competency;

4. fatigue from shift-work;

5. alarm handling;

6. compliance with safety critical procedures;

7. safety culture;

8. communications;

9. ergonomic design of interfaces; and

10. maintenance error.

Each and every topic listed above would benefit from a book in its own right so they are only mentioned here to suggest that human factors covers an enormous number of applications and, through close examination of the business processes, issues can be identified and resolved by those who know best – the workforce. Furthermore, the HSE have updated Regulations, such as the Control of Major Accident Hazards Regulations 1999 (SI 1999/743) (COMAH), and now make it perfectly clear that 'Human Factors' must be taken fully into account in the management of risk.

Accidents over the years

8.26 The improvements that can be achieved in the short-term are a significant reduction in injury rates and at-risk behaviours as shown below. This, coupled with a more open communication and reporting structure based on a 'just' culture, will enable greater interaction and involvement of the workforce leading to further business improvements.

Implementing 'Behavioural Based Safety' processes has always presented a challenge to industry, and until recent years, has often been fragmented or reactive. Increasingly, it is being recognised that a systematic, proactive process that is fully integrated with the management system can add significantly more value by addressing behavioural aspects of safety at the same time as optimising efficiency and productivity issues that have traditionally been considered separate from safety. Moreover, understanding behaviours is critical for the management of change and in the reduction of human errors.

Although many behavioural processes have indeed been successful and considered by practitioners to be proactive, they have not always realised their full potential because they are resource intensive and tend to generate separate committees, separate databases and induce the very unaffordable overload which the majority of businesses cannot tolerate. In addition, the participants never achieve the number of observations (data rate) required to produce statistically significant data. This tends to create even longer delays in providing the very solutions that caused the problems in the first place. Many of the commodity-type processes run out of steam after 12 to 18 months and it is widely recognised that new motivation is required to regenerate increased performance. There is a saying that comes to mind, 'if we always do what we've always done, then we'll always get where we've always got'.

Integration is the key

8.27 Integration highlights the increasing need to move away from a commodity or prescriptive solution and create a process that is owned and developed by each business or even parts of the business. The value that must be added to the management system as a whole is by having a fully integrated process that stimulates discussions on all aspects of the business, whether safety or otherwise, is suitable recorded and an action plan developed for resolution of the issues.

Periodic reviews of these issues and their progress leads to even greater involvement since the workforce can see these issues being addressed. To create a bespoke process that embellishes existing management systems, reduces the strain on existing resources, yet provides data on real-working practices, is fundamental for optimum business performance.

Such an approach that provides a methodology for integrating behavioural safety principles and human factors into existing management systems has been developed. The methodology focuses on the whole organisation and provides a stepped framework that aims to be practical and participative, involving key people with a responsibility for safety of each and every person on site.

In order to capitalise on the need for a systematic, fully-integrated, practical process, it should be recognised that ready-made, off-the-shelf processes only go part of the way towards finding the solution. A bespoke process that embellishes existing management systems and practices that does not put further strain on existing resources or stretch existing systems to breaking point and yet still provides a view of real working practices must be more proactive.

An approach that provides a methodology for integrating behavioural safety principles into existing management systems must be the ideal business solution for any company. The benefits are clear in that resources are freed up, there are fewer committee meetings and more time to develop the action plans.

One of the aims of this breakthrough approach to human factors and, in particular, behavioural change is to transfer the responsibility of the process to the people who actually deal with these issues on a day-to-day basis on each site. By raising awareness of behavioural and human factors issues that directly affect human performance, the site personnel can identify issues beyond the scope of normal auditing and task observation processes and proactively target new areas for improvement that would be missed under normal activities.

The core message is that any team member who has been trained in non-confrontational communications can stimulate a discussion and provide a different perspective on the normal day-to-day working activities without the necessity of additional behavioural or task observations which so often the workforce find difficult or false. The management team must take ownership of the process throughout, with guidance and support to generate a new team approach that is in synergy with the corporate goals and objectives. Accidents do not just happen and the majority of accidents can be prevented because they are caused mainly by:

- human error – 88%

- hardware failures – 10%

- inexplicable – 2%

There is little doubt that the majority of accidents are caused by the activities that people do or fail to do. Acts, omissions and unsafe acts combined with unsafe conditions lead to incidents or accidents. The use of leading indicators such as BBS (behaviour based safety) task observations, incident reports, near miss reports inspections/audits and risk assessments is to create a learning environment upstream of any accident where lessons can be learnt before suffering the pain or trauma of injury. The interaction between unsafe acts and unsafe conditions is clear.

The difficulty with many current systems of audit and inspection together with the BBS process is that they are not joined up – they lack synergy. Tying together unsafe acts and unsafe conditions makes significant gains more quickly than current processes. The discussions leads to action plans that are automatically processed by the management system thus eliminating wasted time and energy, not to mention committee processing by either the BBS or Safety Committees.

Safety leadership is a series of conversations

8.28 Since 'coaching' is a leadership competency, there are five principles that guide respectful conversations that everyone can use.

1. When peers connect, change happens.

2. Ask open information-seeking questions such as: 'How is the job going?' 'Are there any difficulties in completing this task?'

3. Conversations are structured and non-confrontational. Be open to conversations that are unprepared for and focus in the interests of the other person.

4. Investigate how the problems or issues can be resolved. Allow time for the person to get to what is really important. Provide spaces where they can express their doubts and fears by being a thoughtful listener without taking on the responsibility to fix or debate the issue. After all, the person has been invited to talk about what matters to her or him, not the listener, so allow time for the articulation of those thoughts and feelings.

5. Personal transformation happens when the right questions get asked – not by providing answers. When the focus is on the solution, there is an attempt to sell the person something. Allowing people to answer their own questions allows them to discover what they were not aware of and what is needed to move forward. Personal transformation leads corporate transformation, one person at a time.

Human factors integration domains

8.29 By understanding and implementing any of the human factors domains below, and achieving greater understanding of how people interact in the business, will enable a step change in business performance. Open and honest discussions or conversations create a listening and learning organisation that responds to issues and difficulties in the working environment.

A greater involvement by all co-ordinates all workforce communication processes into greater hazard identification and risk management. The existing workforce become more reliable and more focused, and that leads to evolving 'best practice'. Consistency is achieved between similar assets and management are seen to be more visible in their support for safety activities. The regulator has greater trust that human factors issues are being addressed satisfactorily leading to reduced lost workday cases and significantly lower potential for at-risk activities. The management system is more proactive and actions are reviewed, and closed out expediently.

Human factor opportunities

8.30 Some typical examples of human factor opportunities are illustrated in the table below.

Domain	*Issue*	*Topics to consider*
Staffing	How many people are required to operate and maintain the system?	Staffing levels, workload, team organisation, job specification.
Personnel	What are the aptitudes, experience and other human characteristics necessary to operate and maintain the system?	Selection, recruitment and career development. Qualifications and experienced required, general characteristics (body size, strength, eyesight, etc).
Training	How to develop and maintain the requisite knowledge, skills and abilities to operate and maintain the system.	Identifying requirements for new skills, documentation, training courses. Specialist training facilities Individual/team training Skill maintenance (refresher courses, drills).

Domain	Issue	Topics to consider
Human factors engineering (HFE)	How to integrate human characteristics into system design to optimise performance within the human/machine system.	Equipment design, workstation/console design. Workplace layout, maintenance access and ease of maintenance, user interface design. Function allocation between humans and machines. Working environments.
Health hazards	What are the short or long term hazards to health resulting from normal operation of the system?	Exposure to: – toxic materials, electric shock; – mechanical injury, musculoskeletal injury (heavy lifting, repetitive movement); – extreme heat/cold, optical hazards; – electro-magnetic radiation.
System safety	How to avoid the safety risks which humans might cause by operating or maintaining the system abnormally.	Sources of human error. Effects of misuse or abuse. External and environmental hazards.

General methodology

8.31   The general methodology integrates company practices and adapts existing tried-and-tested approaches to reducing the human element of risk, while ensuring that the whole process can be applied with only essential training in non-confrontational communications – see Figure 2. The key process steps are summarised below.

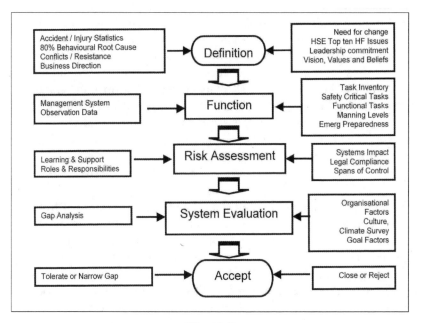

Figure 2

Definition

8.32 The first step is to fully define the reasons for the change. These can be identified within the existing site processes, by a hierachical corporate dictate or a suggestion from the regulator. This definition phase provides the focus for the remaining stages of the process and establishes the activities and the areas that require potential action. This step also clearly defines the goals, where are we going, and expectations in what is to be achieved. It embodies the 'Top Ten Human Factors Issues' from the HSE that are considered essential considerations for a good safety management system. The definition phase also includes those aspects that cannot be changed and are given as non-negotiable. These need to be known at the start of the process so as to avoid duplication of effort during the later stages. This stage is most effective when representation from other business areas within the organisation provides input and it requires visible leadership commitment to ensure that all aspects of change are adequately discussed and ultimately addressed. This stage is also an ideal opportunity for the leadership to share the company vision, values and beliefs that are so critical if everyone is to 'buy-in' to the changes and overcome any residual resistance or legacy conflicts that may reduce the effectiveness of the whole process. A clear statement of the business direction and rationale for the changes is considered the key to success.

In defining the change process, it is essential that accident and injury statistics are shared so that an open commitment to address the root cause issues is seen by the whole workforce. An acknowledgement that 80–95% of all injuries have a behavioural root cause emphasises the importance of human factors in enhancing risk management. A firm understanding that behaviours or 'the way we do business' are critical to creating a lean and mean organisation whilst at the same time changing individual thinking processes towards a safer and efficient productive organisation. The output from this phase provides a firm scenario for subsequent stages.

Function

8.33   Once an inventory of all the related tasks is compiled from all the site procedures, those that are of a safety critical nature can be identified. An additional list of key functional tasks that are essential and non-negotiable is also added at this point Every task can then be 'rated' on the basis of how frequently the task is performed, its duration, how much operator action/intervention is required, together with the likelihood of the worst credible consequence. This rating allows the procedures to be ranked according to their criticality and hence prioritise efforts.

At this stage, consideration should be given to the manning levels, shift patterns, emergency preparedness activities, and any existing task observation processes that are essential for effective running of the management system. A clear input from all business areas is fundamental in defining the minimum that has considered all safety and functional activities.

Risk assessment

8.34   This step consists of several interactive stages that primarily address the systems impact of the proposed changes. Analysis should be made of all the potential risks surrounding the additional roles that people perform in the normal running of their duties and that so often get overlooked.

A multi-disciplined team including health and safety personnel, site managers and human factors professionals should ideally complete any risk assessment. Most importantly, site personnel with experience of the tasks under investigation must be involved throughout this step.

Roles and responsibilities

8.35   The roles and responsibilities of all staff involved with safety critical or functional tasks must be defined or reviewed in light of the proposed changes. It is a unique opportunity to gather detailed information that includes details of the duration of task steps, the environment in which the task is performed and the roles and responsibilities expected of the person performing the task. Any roles or concurrent tasks that have the potential to impact on performance should also have been noted.

Prototype key performance indicators (KPIs)

8.36 The key performance indicators of all staff involved with safety critical or functional tasks must be defined or reviewed in light of the proposed changes. It is another opportunity to gather detailed information upon which someone can be judged to be successful and include safety matrix. However, accidents still occur and so often these indicators are themselves dependent upon others not having an accident. Even in an ideal world where the recordable accident rate is as low as possible, the safety culture is considered excellent and the management are very supportive, people still get hurt. Providing rewards for any activity that could lead to someone taking a shortcut, side stepping a procedure and taking more risk is fundamentally an error of judgement in the extreme, particularly a monetory one. It is clear that we need to have a goal-oriented way by which performance and safety are integrated, but to punish managers and employees for reporting accidents and near misses ignores the prime aim of accident prevention and may lead to a drying up of information or misleading data. However, it is team targets, not individual ones, that produce the best results. Involvement is created through interaction not competition.

Shift information

8.37 A list of shift personnel is compiled outlining their job roles and responsibilities. Any additional duties are noted, for example, first-aider, fire crew or emergency response team. This information outlines the number of people available per shift, any dual roles and whether the team members are multi-skilled. This indicates whether individuals must leave tasks unattended when performing other roles. The information also indicates whether sufficient staff are available, for example to cover breaks. The shift information is simply intended to provide additional information to be considered when evaluating the safeguards. It is also a good indicator of workload issues and fatigue that may generate problems should these issues be ignored. Another requirement that the HSE is keen to see included is a proactive management system.

Spans of control

8.38 There are often areas within the workplace where safety monitoring from a behavioural perspective is limited or considered a low risk. Some commodity processes such as Safe R$^+$ (a trade name for Aubrey Daniels, a US company) suggest pinpoints that are common to all areas of the workplace. This could leave some areas exposed to risk that is not monitored or where there is little safety interaction or awareness. It is desirable – indeed, essential – that all areas in the workplace are involved with safety and that the 'situation awareness', ie the thinking processes, are enhanced to identify potential consequences of actions. This activity is critical if people are to take and use safety knowledge outside the workplace and then start to build a social responsibility for each other and the safety of others.

System evaluation

8.39   The next step is to evaluate the whole system to take into account the organisational culture issues that may prevent or restrict a successful implementation. Specifically, a culture or climate survey may highlight barriers that must be addressed and indicate areas where progress will be less than adequate. This may involve, for example, improving communication channels, procedures and training, prohibiting certain concurrent tasks, improving alarms, increasing staffing levels or introducing engineering controls to avoid human failures resulting in a major accident hazard. It is also important to consult with the operators to explore other potential improvements. An action list is compiled to ensure that all the proposed improvements are allocated to the relevant parties, considered and then either followed through to completion or justification provided as to why the improvement should not be adopted. Therefore, issues such as accessibility, adherence, responsibility for co-ordinating and updating procedures and training can also be taken into consideration.

Acceptance

8.40   The key step of implementation is to agree and commit to all of the objectives in order to demonstrate that human factors issues have been systematically considered. This will require an open communication process with all the stakeholders so that there is a common understanding of the key deliverables from the outset. A proactive, committed champion or change agent is key to success of the change process. This key role is the core in understanding the part that human factors and, in particular, behaviours play in accident causation and can verify actions, communicate changes and ultimately challenge the change process, objectives and identify process gaps along the way.

Sustainability

8.41   Only when there is total involvement, interaction and participation between everyone in the company, on a day-to-day basis, will it produce a more effective, efficient and safe organisation (see the flowchart in **Appendix B**). In an ever-changing environment, organisations are under constant pressure to find new solutions that will preserve future competitiveness. The difficulty is compounded by uncertainty of the future and constant change in values. There is a constant demand to move towards a proactive attitude and a need for new management principles and developing organisational learning. That said, it is often very difficult to let go of old ways and methods because they did work.

Why organisational learning?

8.42 Organisational learning is the process by which the organisation's knowledge and value base changes, leading to improved problem solving and capacity for action. It is unique to an organisation and takes place through individuals and their interactions with each other. Organisational learning is characterised by the collective thinking and the creation of a shared frames of reference. The emphasis being not on individual learning but on the processes that make binding decisions and brings about agreement as to the way forward. The development of a collective view of reality depends on mutual understanding through non-confrontational communications and simple language. Without this critical path being followed, the knowledge of individuals is severely restricted and not available to the organisation ('know how').

Communication is not, however, sufficient in itself. If individual knowledge is to be transferred into organisation knowledge, there is a need for transparency and integration of group processes. This is where leadership is so critical, supported by non-confrontational communication. Without either, the journey is more difficult. Nobody knows the workplace better than those who experience it and the associated risks, at every working moment. This know-how is 'gold dust' when it starts to be used for the good of everyone. One of the aims of this breakthrough approach to human factors and, in particular, the management of change, was to transfer the skills and knowledge to the people who actually deal with these issues on a day-to-day basis on each site. By raising awareness of behavioural and human factors issues that can directly affect human performance, the site personnel can identify issues beyond the scope of normal auditing and task observation processes and proactively target new areas for improvement that would be missed under normal processes.

The core message is that any team member can provide a different perspective on the normal day-to-day working activities without the necessity of additional observation processes. The management team must take ownership of the process throughout, with guidance and support. This encourages the team to use the training that has been provided and to explore human factors and behavioural issues on every site. The process illustrates how simple, practical and effective methods can be used to assess how human failures contribute to risk. This approach is flexible enough to incorporate existing hazard identification and risk assessment information. For companies where previous evaluations of alarm systems, control systems, staffing levels and procedures have been conducted, these could be included. Therefore, the flexibility within this approach can avoid the need to revisit issues and perform repeat assessments. However, it is important to ensure that any previous assessments used within this approach are still relevant to the current tasks and current task environment. If minor changes to the site or the tasks have occurred since the previous assessments were conducted, then a partial update may be sufficient.

Chapter 9

Implementing and Developing Corporate Leadership

Introduction

9.0   The focus of this book is on safety leadership management and not just management. By adopting management techniques without safety leadership from the top there will never be a real health and safety culture. Only by real leadership will the corporate culture encompass health and safety. This chapter makes an examination of the leadership issue. Of course, many undertakings state that they have health and safety as a priority, but how many health and safety professionals do you know who are members of a board of directors? Finance directors are common but safety directors are very rare. Conversely, how many directors do you know who have any competency in health and safety? The answer is likely to be not many, if, indeed, there are any. How many health and safety advisors do you know that report directly to a senior-level member of the board or its equivalent? Generally, there is a buffer that stops direct contact and the only concern is when there is an incident and information is required at a senior level. There may well be accountants and lawyers as board members but when there is an incident and lives are lost, the advice from them will be as to how much it is going to cost and how best to defend any legal action.

The aim of this book is to develop senior-level leaders who accept the legal and accountancy advice but also have an equally competent health and safety professional either on the board or working along side it with full and direct access. Even with advice the leaders must drive safety and accept that responsibility and accountability for safety is a line management function. Without adopting the leadership concept, an undertaking may be making the right noises, have the pieces of paper, but no ownership, and without ownership there is little or no trust and that leads to limited co-operation – all of which leads to accidents.

Senior management responsibilities

9.1   With the introduction of corporate killing and the individual offences, the adoption of a corporate governance structure, for any organisation no matter its size or type, must be considered as being a valuable if not vital tool available to management. As part of an organisation's corporate health and safety management system the Health and Safety Commission (HSC) introduced the guidance 'Directors Responsibilities for Health and Safety' (INDG343) for board members of all types of organisations. The objective is to ensure that risks to employees and those not employed are properly managed, and the focus is on company directors to establish effective management of health and safety risks with emphasis on the following key issues:

- to maximise the well being and productivity of all people working for an organisation;

- stop people getting injured, ill or killed through work activities;

- improve the organisation's reputation in the eyes of customers, competitors, suppliers, other stakeholders and the wider community;

- avoid damaging effects on turnover and profitability;

- encourage better relationships with contractors and more effective contracted activities;

- minimise the likelihood of prosecution and consequent penalties.

It is important to note that while the guidance uses the term 'director' to indicate a member of the board, the guidance applies to other undertakings that do not have to have a director to comply with the law. Therefore, the guidance must be deemed to apply to trust executives, trustees, partners, etc. The guidance is not compulsory and undertakings are free to take other action, but if they follow the guidance, they will generally be doing enough to comply with the law and, in the legal sense, the guidance can be used to illustrate good practice.

There are five action points which identify that the board needs to accept formally and publicly its collective role in providing health and safety leadership for its organisation. The board needs to ensure that all of its decisions reflect its health and safety intentions, as described in the health and safety policy statement. It needs to recognise its role in engaging the active participation of workers in providing health and safety and must ensure that it is kept informed of, and alert to, relevant health and safety risk management issues. The HSC recommends that boards appoint one member of the board to be the health and safety director.

It is the last action that has evoked most comments and concerns as many directors and organisations see the appointed director as being the 'scapegoat' for the board when things go wrong. The HSC and the Health and Safety Executive (HSE) point out that there is no intention for an individual to be exposed for the failings of the board, providing that the individual who has responsibility for health and safety has not been negligent. The director appointed – and the HSC would ideally like to see the Chairman, Chief Executive or the head of an undertaking appointed to that role, – must ensure that an effective and positive system for health and safety is in place within the organisation.

Ten-Minute Rule Bill

9.2   Ross Cranston QC MP has drafted a Ten-Minute Rule Bill that would impose duties on directors. It proposes to take the HSC's 'Directors Responsibilities for Health and Safety' guidance forward into legislation. The Bill would require companies to appoint a director as the health and safety director, and to impose duties on this director and on other directors of companies in relation to health and safety, and for connected purposes. The draft Bill, defined as the Company Directors' (Health and Safety) Bill makes the following provisions.

- *Health and Safety Directors*

    Every company other than a private company shall appoint one of its directors as the health and safety director and will provide the name of the health and safety director of the company.

- *Directors' duties regarding health and safety*

    It is the duty of the directors of a company to exercise their powers and to discharge their duties in the interests of the health and safety of its employees and others affected by its operations. The directors of a company are to take effective steps to ensure that the company acts in accordance with the obligations imposed on it by any applicable law relating to health and safety. The directors of a company are to be taken to meet the requirements if they act reasonably and in good faith. This will require them to inform themselves about the company's health and safety obligations in the particular circumstances of its operations and consider any report of a health and safety director that has been appointed. The health and safety director will need to:

    (a)   monitor on a regular basis the health and safety performance of the company;

(b)   ensure the health and safety statement of the company reflects current board priorities on the matter;

(c)   ensure that the company's management systems provide for effective monitoring and reporting of its health and safety performance;

(d)   report to other directors immediately on any significant health and safety failure in the company and on recommendations for changes; and

(e)   report to the board on the health and safety implications of its decisions.

The duties of the health and safety director shall not affect in any way the duties which the board has given to other directors with respect to health and safety matters, and the duties of directors regarding health and safety matters are imposed under the Act.

The Bill has not progressed at the time of writing but is indicative to the high-level activity of a number of Members of Parliament to progress health and safety issues to the front of the political agenda.

Leadership by example

9.3   E I Du Pont demonstrated safety leadership when forming the scienced-based company, 'DuPont', and insisted powder mills were spaced apart to minimise the spread of fire or explosion and the mills were designed to direct a blast upward. These initiatives successfully limited costly damage and minimised injuries and, importantly, this helped DuPont retain its more experienced workers and safety-conscious workers who could use their knowledge to help prevent further incidents and recognise warning signs of danger.

During the nineteenth century, DuPont, a company recognised today for its positive safety culture, was driving safety. It was achieved through both personal stewardship and the issuance of safety rules which, by 1811, had been put into writing and circulated widely. In a true demonstrable act of safety leadership after an explosion in 1818, the members of the DuPont family, who were away at the time of the explosion, agreed that one partner should always remain in the yards and that lower-level managers reside as they did on plant grounds.

When Lammot DuPont moved to involve the company in dynamite production during the 1880s he realised production risks would be increased but could be mitigated by mechanisation. In the twentieth century Lewis De Blois encouraged DuPont to formalise its safety initiatives and headed up the company's first safety office. In 1911 the company formed a focal point for the introduction of safety devices and organised prevention of accident commissions in each department. The following year the company began keeping full records of all accidents, which displayed a steady downward trend.

Individual safety leadership was clearly demonstrated in DuPont from the outset and today the company remains concerned for the health and safety of its employees and this is ingrained in DuPont's structure and corporate culture.

➢ **Help Point:** The DuPont web site can be found at www.dupont.com

Benefits of effective reporting

9.4 By way of comparison, there are 850,000 adverse incidents happening each year within NHS hospitals. These mistakes are estimated to cost the health service in excess of £2 billion annually. Moreover, there are an estimated 34,000 preventable deaths in the NHS annually (Henderson 2002). The Government has recently introduced an 'early warning system' to detect medical errors. The system will require all medical errors or near misses to be recorded in a central register. The register will be used to allow errors to be analysed and enable steps to be taken to ensure the same mistakes do not happen again. This demonstrates the difference between DuPont, where the management drove the safety culture, and our 'health care' service where it required the government to intervene and introduce a system for safety improvement based on their record of accidents commenced in 1912.

Whilst the reporting and investigation of accidents is important to improve safety performance, it is still very much a lagging indicator of safety. An equally important leading indicator is the reporting of near misses/hits, which demands a stronger culture for employees to admit to failures which can cause limited or no damage.

An effective investigation into all incidents will help to:

- demonstrate concern and assure personnel that action will be taken;

- find the root causes;

- prevent recurrence;

- identify trends.

All incidents/accidents must be fully investigated to assess their true potential/severity.

People may not report incidents/accidents either because of fear or they did not know they should report accidents or because of previous bad experiences.

Where the company is being led by a committed safety leader and a positive culture is developing, people should:

- be instructed to report an incident/accident with simple systems in place for reporting and recording;

- have it demonstrated to them that an open safety culture exists, eg a just system;

- be encouraged by example;

- be encouraged by management responding positively.

A company with a positive safety culture will be monitoring *all* incidents and observing trends. When a senior manager takes on a new enterprise it is essential that the safety performance and reputation of the company is immediately reviewed. For example, in the oil industry it can certainly have a substantial influence on the ability to trade profitably and for contractors to win contracts from the clients.

Safety performance

9.5 An understanding of the safety performance can immediately be gained from the lagging indicators of safety performance but, more importantly, the safety culture of the company can be determined from the effort made to undertake proactive measures, the leading indicators and the measurable effort of the current management team to lead the safety programmes in the company. What if the outgoing MD had, on a routine basis, personally undertaken to ensure the safety of his or her own employees and any other stakeholder or third party whose people and assets could be put at risk by his/her operations?

A review of safety committee meetings will give a view on how effectively issues raised were being resolved. A review of trends in the near miss reports will appraise the new management for any immediate actions required where poor safety trends are identified. A high ratio of near miss reports to incidents provides high numbers of learning opportunities from which to resolve any issues. It is important to talk to the company safety professionals and determine their attitude and the leadership they have received from the top management.

The safety professionals are not responsible for the safety performance within an organisation; they are there to give professional support to the senior management. If any of the teams consider that accidents 'just' happen then there is a great deal of work to be undertaken because all accidents should be considered a result of management failure. It is necessary to talk, on a personal basis, with members of the workforce and safety representatives. As a result, the leader will be able to determine their impressions of the importance of safety in the management agenda and whether they think it is 'profit at all cost'. Hopefully, it will not be necessary to review prosecutions and improvement notices but this is another obvious measure of performance. All of these reviews will be available internally for an immediate view.

An external view on a company's safety performance can also be determined and the HSE are keen to give advice as this is preferable to prosecution and they will offer a view on the company's performance. Although the HSE and local government inspectors are very busy, consider inviting the local inspector into the workplace and gather his/her views on the measures the company has in place.

The authors, having gained experience from the regulatory regime and the contracting industry, appreciate the additional effort required to maintain safety performance during periods of change in corporations. When talking to a workforce it transpires that their prime concern is with job security and safety is lower on their agenda, that is, until the realisation that an injury from an industrial accident affects their ability to earn a living. The regulators in the oil industry have been quick to respond to corporate change and have been keen to offer proactive advice. It has been beneficial for the regulator and corporation to work together at such times to maintain and improve standards. Undertaking a safety seminar during a merger process can put across the determination of new management to drive safety positively and a view from the regulator on legal responsibilities of the whole workforce provides a powerful message. A professional trade association may also rank your company's safety performance.

The aspects of a positive safety culture must be expressed in both human and commercial terms. Safety performance assessment packages are available from the HSE and the British Safety Council, which if answered honestly, will give a realistic assessment of the effectiveness of the company's safety systems. A university's industrial psychology group could undertake a confidential review of the workforce's attitude to safety, which can be particularly revealing. For instance, a director of a major offshore oil and gas producer was very open recently and publicly expressed his surprise that the workforce considered production came before safety. This was, of course, one of the contributory factors in the *Piper Alpha* disaster which claimed 167 lives. Having conducted these surveys, the company must implement immediate improvements to its systems. The subcontractors and other stakeholders will have a view on the company's performance, therefore, it is helpful to meet with other managing directors in order to discuss this. A company's reputation will be rapidly degraded if subcontractors' staff are not treated with the same care as the company's own staff.

The listening safety leader will always be able to learn from his peers in his industry. For example, the UK managing director of a world-class offshore drilling contractor made over 70 visits to the Aberdeen heliport at all hours of the day to speak personally with his offshore crews, stressing the safety first message and demonstrating true leadership through his actions. Ultimately, safety can provide a competitive edge and is obviously a reflection of the management system's training and competence of the workforce. It is often said that the workforce is a company's most valuable asset – so why injure them?

As previously discussed, poor safety can also cause a company to fail, however, in the authors' experience there has never been an issue with competitors sharing best safety practise, which is commendable and can help prevent company failure. The dedicated safety leader will also take the time to actively involve themselves in any industry initiatives, such as the 'Step Change In Safety' initiative in the UK oil and gas industry which undertook some extremely effective work to improve the industry's overall performance. The client can also benefit by promoting the sharing of best practise. As the oil and gas industry moved into the hostile deep waters of the Atlantic Sea, west of Shetland, there were new environmental conditions to contend with which were new to the industry and proved challenging.

Initial safety performance was disappointing and the asset manager responsible for developing the new fields made the leadership move to call in all his main contractors to share their experiences, good and bad, and learn from them. This went as far as calling in some former special services personnel who had established a company to aid all personnel to use techniques to shift loads effectively. The trainers had obviously been trained in martial arts and knew how to use their bodies effectively and it was interesting to see a group of directors efficiently moving loads around the conference room after this manual handling training. There was a wide range of management representative at these forums including drilling contractors, aviation representatives, scaffolding contractors, caterers and standby vessel managers, all sharing their safety experiences, failures and successes – a real learning experience. These meetings were always informative and were always a priority in the schedule of a safety leader.

Management hierarchial levels

9.6   It is considered that in most undertakings there are three hierarchial levels of management. The first is the corporate (senior level) management, which includes directors, partners or others at a similar level in an undertaking. The second level is the middle management who are the interface between the senior management and the supervisory level of management. The third level comprises the first-line managers often known as supervisors, team leaders or foremen.

There is no doubt that senior managers are the key influence on an undertaking's safety management. This is supported by the HSE ('Revitalising our potential', HSC, 2000) who state:

> 'poor management and ignorance of good practices... the primary reasons for health and safety failures'.

This means that it is imperative that senior managers are proactive in establishing the safety culture in the undertaking. The HSE, in 'The cost to Britain of workplace accidents and work related ill health in 1995/1996' again identifies the need for management to get onboard with safety and state:

> 'Senior management commitment is crucial to a positive health and safety culture. It is best indicated by the disposition of resources (time, money, people) and support allocated to health and safety management and by the status given to health and safety'.

It is likely that the behaviour associated with effectiveness at corporate management level will be different to those that will be important at the level of the site manager, which in turn will be different from those at the level of the first-line supervisor. Higher-level mangers are usually more concerned with strategy, for example, making long-range plans, formulating policy, modifying the organisation's structure, and initiating new ways of doing things. Decisions at this level usually have a long-term perspective. Middle-level management, such as site managers, are primarily concerned with tactics such as interpreting and implementing policies and programmes, and they usually have a moderately long-term perspective of one to three years. Low-level managers, such as supervisors and team leaders, are primarily concerned with operational matters, for example structuring, co-ordinating and facilitating work activities, and that occurs on a day-to-day basis.

Management v employees' perceptions

9.7 Management v employees' perceptions of the organisation's philosophy of either production or safety is the second most important factor after corporate safety policies. Companies that have good safety records tend to be more productive and it requires safety leadership to convince the workforce that the development of a positive health and safety culture can improve performance and efficiency. In developing a positive safety culture they can maintain and even enhance production.

The opposite is that perceptions of high performance can lead workers to believe that the adoption of short-cut behaviour is expected, or required, as part of the job. This means that the workers who perceive a high degree of performance pressure will focus their attention on completing the work and focus less on the safety of their workplace procedures. Workers should be encouraged to stop work if they consider an operation puts them or others at risk.

Employees will have a perception of their organisations values and beliefs which must clearly show that the company is committed to them: thus an obligation develops aimed at benefiting the organisation. In an undertaking with positive motives, the beneficial actions have been shown to include employees engaging to improve the organisation and performing better. Employee evaluation of the social support given to them by managers and supervisors is also an important factor with regard to their satisfaction with safety measures in the workplace. The most important factor is management commitment and involvement in safety in the workplace.

The human element of good management in organisations values industrial relations where there is frequent and positive contact with employees. It has been shown that a management, which has a high regard and shows concern for its employees and treats them with respect regarding their work, will find a workforce that feels appreciated as individuals with a belief that their contribution is valuable to the organisation.

High levels of open communication and interaction between workers and management can be identified with positive leadership. Participative management and time spent by management communicating at the worksite are associated with good safety performance. Top performing companies provide direct and immediate channels of communication and positive employee/management interaction using some form of immediate feedback to motivate their employees.

More than forty years ago Heinrich advised:

'The supervisor or foreman is the key man in industrial accident prevention. His application of the art of supervision to the control of worker performance is the factor of greatest influence in successful accident prevention'.

Positive management safety leadership means that there will be high quality and supportive supervision and that will enhance positive safety outcomes. It is the employees' perceptions of organisational support and quality of communication that will lead to employees' being willing to engage in safety discussions and enhance safety commitments, which in turn will reduce accident rates.

Supervisors who tend to use a more participative management style and who place importance on team work and recognise safety as an important aspect of their role are more effective. Supervisors who do not value their staff and do not have a participatory attitude will have safety low on the agenda, if at all. They will operate in an environment of distrust and have a policing system of supervision.

Corporate culture

9.8   The workforce needs to see a just culture and that requires trust with clear and defined lines of what is, and what is not, acceptable behaviour. Worker safety will be higher when supervisors have the appropriate authority to influence decisions that affect the safety of those in their care by involving them in accident prevention activities. To achieve this, senior management needs to encourage involvement and participation between supervisors and employees with regard to health and safety. Therefore, managers and supervisors have different but complimentary roles in the management of health and safety in the workplace. Managers have a wide range of influence over corporate outcomes in general while supervisors have a narrower sphere of influence. However, being closer to the workforce will have a greater direct influence on health and safety issues. The provision of suitable training is a requirement for management to identify and manage so as to develop their employees' skills to enable them to undertake their duties in a competent and safe manner. The individual should fit the job and the job should fit with the employee's abilities.

Safety suggestions and ideas raised by the workforce should get serious attention and consideration. Obtaining this information is so often achieved through an anonymous system because many workers do not want to be identified for putting forward a suggestion. However, where trust levels are high, some organisations have monetary reward systems that encourage workforce input. It is crucial that management seeks an input from safety and health committees in helping to address health and safety issues.

Morale is a key issue and undertakings with a positive health and safety culture have a high level of morale through good safety management. Poor morale is directly related to management failure to adopt safe systems of work and involve lower levels of management and the workforce in health and safety issues.

Leadership factors

9.9   The important message when looking at good management is to identify leadership where there is a commitment to safety and that involves the clear adoption of safety attitudes and safety practices. It is not sufficient to make bold statements or produce systems if there is a perceived lack of safety leadership from the top. Such statements and procedures will be rendered as meaningless where the leadership actions do not match the words and will not aid the development of a safety culture within an undertaking.

Good safety leadership qualities will actively create a foundation where worker safety takes precedence over all other matters, including production. This is supported by active involvement of senior management as a motivational force for both line management and employees. The objective is to promote the concept of safe activities being associated with good safety performance. The more that safety management is fully integrated into the running of the business (the management system) and is considered as a business process, the more responsive will be the whole undertaking. Senior management leadership will focus on a number of proactive activities including giving positive recognition for a good job or performance. Coupled with this, is the recognition that the individual knows the job best and his knowledge and know-how coupled with their understanding of the corporate goals is crucial in the process of meeting those goals.

A key aspect of good safety leadership behaviour is to empower subordinates within the decision-making process which will develop middle management and supervisors with a sense of ownership and ensure continued professional development. This leads to participative, supportive and trust relationships and ownership in the undertaking. Without these factors there is management, but no safety leadership.

Trust and ownership

9.10   There must be trust with top management in the way it gives priority to safety goals over production goals and workers' acceptance of the organisations objectives. Trust links into numerous aspects of the undertaking and includes the quality of communication, staff performance and behaviour, problem solving and co-operation. This means that managerial behaviour is important in the development of trust in the employee-manager relationships.

Where there is a serious impediment to safety and health conditions it may well come from the ownership of safety being delegated down to safety advisors who sometimes lack the authority to impose safety on work procedures. Ownership and leadership starts at the very top and if the senior management are not seen to be actively leading and participating, then the culture is doomed to failure. Good leadership will encompass ownership and will be measured by a greater priority afforded to safety and the belief that all accidents are preventable. The failure to have effective leadership in safety at work can create the feeling that individuals' efforts are hindered by senior management, which can result in higher accident rates.

Ownership is a key factor with undertakings that have cultures of open communication; valuing people will show greater trustworthy behaviour, particularly delegating control, communicating openly and showing concern. This should then encourage trust in management behaviour through the structuring of general patterns of communication, co-ordination and decision-making.

Leadership commitment

9.11   Management has to lead and be seen to lead and demonstrate its commitment to safety. Those leadership skills will encompasses a wide range of factors and, in particular, include management behaviours from the development of a safety programme to the quality of employee management relations.

Senior management must develop the undertaking's rules and regulations and regularly update them. It is also important that both management and staff comply with them and the employees should be involved as the rules will protect them. Management should undertake formal inspections of the workplace or sites at regular and frequent intervals. Management cannot condone unsafe acts, therefore, it is important that management is involved with the thorough investigation of all accidents and near misses and that there is a system for record keeping and passing on lessons learned from incident investigations to all staff. Management must encourage good housekeeping and environmental conditions as well as provide good and relevant training to ensure a competent workforce, and that includes everybody employed in the undertaking. A high priority must be given to safety at any company meeting and it is imperative that in larger undertakings there is an active safety committee involving a high-ranking safety advisor, preferably at board level. This shows that there is a commitment to safety through management attitudes, behaviours and styles of leadership which will have a powerful influence on workforce safety motivation. The objective is to show an open, active and genuine concern for safety on the part of management. Through positive leadership, workplace safety initiatives combine with worker motivation to promote co-operation. The objective is to develop a positive team spirit and willingness to co-operate with other team members and other teams in order to achieve the undertaking's goals. The problem is that there are many managers, but few good leaders.

Undertakings with clear safety goals tend to be more productive and, for senior management to increase workers safety motivation, they must increase supervisors and workers capacity to actively co-operate with each other. This means that with the evolving leadership role, management participation and involvement in safety activities are important but so is the extent that management encourages involvement of the workforce, who must be permitted to help shape interventions rather that simply playing a passive role of compliance. A decentralised approach to safety management has been shown to be the most effective way in which management can promote workforce safety motivation and develop a culture where workers take ownership and responsibility for safety and become actively motivated to take personal initiatives in safety. The objective is to develop a positive team spirit and willingness to co-operate with other team members and other teams in order to achieve the undertaking's goals.

Senior management leadership

9.12   It is clear that senior management must develop a style of leadership that is positive and invokes trust. The old adage that actions speak louder than words is paramount. When the highest level of management says one thing but does another, or uses fear motivation or bullying techniques, then the element of trust is lost. Safety and health within the undertaking should not be a visible stand-alone concept, but should be integral to the corporate culture and be seen to be as important as competitiveness and profitability. In the 'senior management leadership' concept, the three elements of leadership, safety and trust are interlinked as being of equal importance and parity. This is important because with a situation of strong leadership but very limited trust, the balance is offset and the concept of senior management leadership is not effective.

There is truth in the concept that the day employees do not consider they are able to raise issues and problems with regard to health and safety openly is the day that the leader has become ineffective. They will rightly or wrongly have concluded that the leader does not care about their problems or that the leader is not prepared to help them. It is essential that barriers are not put in place to deter upward or two-way communication from the workforce. Their views should be taken into account so they feel valued. If employees are denied access to senior management either directly or through their line management then they may be denied valued input which can help their decision making process.

Without this direction and guidance the employees may choose to undertake actions in good faith that could result in an incident. In this situation if things do go wrong there is likely to be a cover up and it will be difficult to encourage a learning organisation in a regime where communication does not flow openly between workforce and management. The key message is that effective leaders are both visible and available. Leaders will listen and learn, face the challenges and this will result in a culture where problem solving replaces blame.

Change in an undertaking is a dynamic process but when senior management instigates change for the sake of change or because it is the 'thing to do', then it creates confusion, credibility is lost and a financial cost can result through lost productivity because change is disruptive. The leader will consider the need for change objectives and focus on reaching the goal, drawing the whole team with him or her. Leaders explain the need for change and, in some cases, allow managers a free reign, while in other situations they will monitor closely. They will actively encompass health and safety and welfare advice so that it becomes an endemic part of the culture and a consideration in the change process and not an afterthought.

The management of change, either through takeovers or mergers, often identifies difficulties, particularly with individuals in new roles with new responsibilities. Often the changes mean a dilution in numbers of staff and that can impact on safety within the organisation. The changes are often implemented quickly, without a clear understanding of the impact on each individual's performance; competencies are often weak, workload and fatigue often increase.

The analysis of safety critical tasks and competencies is critical to eliminate potential hazardous situations. In order to reduce the impact of change, good communication is essential to provide an awareness of the need for change and a strong leadership desire to make the change happen and to ensure that everyone has the right knowledge and skills.

The effect on an undertaking by a good leader's enthusiasm and optimism is powerful, while management who engender cynicism and pessimism are damaging. It must be remembered that what flows down from the top rests at the bottom. This is evidenced where management have ignored the philosophy that good health and safety leads to efficiency and can improve on profitability. Whatever title the top person in an organisation adopts, be it Chairman, Managing Director, Chief Executive, Principal Partner, that person is where the 'buck' stops. There can be participative management and bottom-up employee involvement but ultimately it leads to the 'controlling mind' of the undertaking.

The leader will have to listen to conflicting opinions of management and/or employees and will often have to make the final decision which may not be readily accepted by the workforce. Such decisions must be well informed and health and safety is an important consideration in this decision process and an uninformed decision can easily have a detrimental impact on the health and safety culture. Ideally, all employees must have a positive attitude toward health and safety and this is an important component in the recruitment, induction and performance review process.

If there is no safety leadership, then productivity and profitability are the only objectives of the company and the selection and promotion process will preclude the considerations of health and safety and the poor culture can be self-perpetuating. If there is a director on the board with a clearly defined responsibility for health and safety, this will send a clear message to the workforce that health and safety is a priority for the company. Good leaders know that the health and safety and welfare of the workforce are key factors in modern business success.

Middle management leadership

9.13 While the senior management are the 'controlling minds' of the undertaking, middle management are tasked with implementing the senior management's objectives. The middle management have an essential role to play in the communication path as the senior management find it more difficult to spend time with the workforce as the company grows. It is essential, therefore, that middle management clearly understands that health and safety ranks as a corporate performance measure on the same level as production output and profitability.

At all levels of management and supervision the link between good safety and good business must be clear. They must appreciate the effect poor health and safety performance can have on corporate reputation, the possible loss of revenue if customers lose trust and the reduction in profits in the longer term as insurance premiums increase.

Supervisory leadership

9.14   Effective supervisors are trusted and recognise that health and safety is an integral part of the corporate culture and carry forward the concept of openness, participation and teamwork. Supervisors hold an important place in the corporate structure, being involved in the planning and influencing decision making whilst controlling the workforce. They fill the gap between management and those carrying the work activities. They need to be fair, participative and value the workforce they are responsible for. Therefore, it is critical that to be effective managers they must communicate and display leadership, in particular, when difficult or complex issues have to be dealt with.

Supervisors will generally have more detailed knowledge of hazards and the risk status. Providing that they recognise that safety is a major part of their job they should have the trust of the workforce and, in turn, they should have the trust of management. A failure in this important link can be failure in corporate health and safety practice.

Leadership for employees

9.15   The critical element in the evolution of effective health and safety practice is the participation of the employees, ie the workforce. Failure to encompass the individuals or team members into a corporate safety culture will leave the undertaking exposed. Those at the lower end of the corporate structure depend upon effective leadership, good communication and trust. A failure of any one of these renders the culture ineffective, resulting in 'no interest', low moral and poor output or productivity situation. When these events occur, health and safety standards reduce and accidents or serious incidents occur.

Often, the workforce looks to the senior management as the 'bosses' with the proviso that they know best and are to be obeyed. Where there is a culture of blind obedience, the undertaking is open to failure, particularly with regard to health and safety, and not forgetting that it is a legal requirement to involve the people being protected. Where a workforce is not empowered or trained there may be no perception or appreciation of risk when directed to follow health and safety procedures and they may resist utilising personal protective equipment. It follows that leadership is not about giving instruction. Leaders must lead by example supported by innovative health and safety training. These are key elements in the culture development process.

Requirement for leadership from the outset

9.16   A statement often made in business is 'your greatest asset is your people'. It is obvious from the injury and fatalities that occur in industry that more can be done to support this statement.

The health and welfare of employees in smaller undertakings is of particular significance as the loss of an employee's services can have a significant effect upon the performance of the company. Small undertakings have to comply with the same extensive safety legislation as a larger entity, often without the support of an in-house safety professional. In this situation, effective safety training for employees is essential so that they have a better awareness of the risks in the business and, therefore, are more able to protect themselves. The first person to undertake a safety training programme should be the 'controlling mind' of the undertaking. As the undertaking grows, the effective leader will benefit from the investment in safety training as the employees will be looking out for each other and the leader can take the time to focus on critical issues and continue to balance the well being of both the undertaking and the staff to obtain a positive outcome for all.

Therefore, early investment in health and safety training will pay dividends as companies grow and employees are promoted. In addition to the drive, expertise and determination they have to succeed, they will have an appreciation of the need to protect the most important asset – the employees. The safety leader has set the example, invested in training and the positive culture will grow with the undertaking ensuring that good safety is good business.

Chapter 10

The 'Wingate' Leadership Concept

Introduction

10.0 There are many who consider themselves to be leaders but, in fact, there are few who can be allocated the title of a true leader, a person who is a meticulous planner, organiser and an inspiring leader. This requires a person who can identify a project, locate the 'right' management, prepare the plan, meet the demands of the people involved, and carry it through to a successful outcome then review the successes and failures and learn for the future. It is necessary to go back to the Second World War where there was a remarkable achievement for what was said to be an impossible task because it was against overwhelming odds. The exploits of Brigadier General Orde Wingate have, when examined, been related to leadership management and cross-referenced to health and safety and is now known as the Wingate leadership concept.

It was 1942, wartime, and involved one of the most hostile areas of our planet, the Burmese jungle. There was death, sickness and injury but this was the key for Wingate to plan, train and lead a force of second line troops and engage the enemy in what was to be the first long-range penetration deep behind the enemy's lines, not with a small commando-style raid, but a force of 3,000 troops. To gain an insight into the military exploits of Orde Wingate, two excellent books have been referenced: Charles J Rollo, *Wingate's Raiders* (Viking Press, 1944) and David Rooney, *Wingate and the Chindits: Redressing the Balance* (Cassell Military Paperbacks, 2000).

The leader

10.1 The leader was Brigadier Orde Wingate, an army officer whose exploits in the Second World War were synonymous with Lawrence of Arabia. Both were incredible leaders, but while Lawrence would buy the power of armies, Wingate would engage those who would fight for their own end and lead them. Wingate is best known for establishing and leading the Chindits, the name given to the soldiers who carried out daring raids deep behind enemy lines in the Burmese Jungle.

In 1942, the allied armies in the Far East were being beaten by the Japanese who were withdrawing and, in many cases, surrendering to what was a superior enemy and masters at jungle warfare. The senior allied commanders were becoming negative in thought and action; a situation that cascaded down through the ranks. The enemy was operating against conventional armies that moved and received supplies by road and railway, and the Japanese won by the simple device of infiltration. To halt the pending disaster it required a radical approach and that involved Wingate, who had a brilliant military mind but above all was a leader.

He arrived in India in 1942 with a plan of long-range penetration involving a revolutionary system of training, transportation, communication and supply. The conventional way of war was for troops to move forward with long supply columns following. This was evidenced in the Gulf War and it was shown that on a number of occasions the advance had to stop to allow re-supply to catch up and it was also evidenced that those supply lines were often disrupted by the enemy. It also involves a lot of manpower and transport. Wingate's plan was to train and take 3,000 men 200 miles behind enemy lines through impenetrable jungle and, for three months, attack the enemy's own supply bases and supply lines as well as destroy railways and bridges.

Wingate's leadership qualities meant that he trained his men in jungle warfare, under conditions as gruelling as anything they might encounter in the operation, until every one of them was a hardened, cunning, self-reliant jungle fighter. Medicine was not as we know it today and so he trained his troops to look after their personal hygiene, health and fitness. Sickness and injury were, and indeed even today is, a fact of life in the jungle environment. He would administer treatment personally and so by example he prepared the unit for what they would face. The versatile helicopter was still the figment of conception and so there would be no rapid evacuation of sick or wounded soldiers; they would where possible carve runways out of the jungle to allow conventional aircraft to land and take off. One of the lessons learned was the need to evacuate wounded and sick troops. Future operations would involve air evacuation.

On the ground, his force would rely on the jungle for cover and so the force avoided roads and established tracks. Transport would be through the use of pack animals to include elephants, mules and bullocks. He would divide his force into highly mobile, self-contained columns and infiltrate through the Japanese lines, devastating military installations and wrecking the enemy's whole system of communications in Northern Burma. His own communication lines would be invulnerable to enemy attack because he would have none – at least not in the orthodox sense. All his supplies would be dropped from the air and wireless would provide his only contact with the outside world. With these tactics he was prepared to operate indefinitely against odds of more than ten to one deep inside enemy-occupied territory.

He called his men 'Chindits' after the Chinthey – the mythological beast, half-lion, half-griffin, statues of which stand guard over Burmese pagodas to ward off evil spirits. The lion-griffin symbolised the unique co-operation between ground and air forces. His leadership extended to being an expert in scientific nutrition and before the operation he would carefully weigh the respective food values to provide the most effective diet. He also engaged Burmese soldiers into the unit who were masters at survival in the jungle and taught what wildlife and vegetation could be eaten. On the way out at the end of the operation the survival skills were to be valuable. He was a master of propaganda and had a genius for winning co-operation from the natives of a country. He always carried with him a duplicating machine, a loudspeaker and a unit of specially trained local propagandists. Communication extended beyond his own troops but to the enemy as well as the local population. A major failing in modern business is where the senior management fails to communicate.

Opposition to his plan by many senior officers who had, and were, faced with defeat was his biggest barrier, but there were those who had the vision to see the potential. The main concerns focused on the fact that a fairly junior officer proposed a high-risk venture that was unorthodox and not in the rulebook. There was the issue of valuable troops being committed to such an operation and there were the potential losses of troops in battle to injury and disease. They doubted whether the re-supply plan would work and they doubted the value of the plan even if it succeeded. However, Wingate was an unusual leader and adopted what could be considered to be the 'health and safety leadership' option.

Hazard identification

Wingate leadership

10.2 The first thing Wingate did was to send for every available book on the training and tactics of the enemy, the religion and customs of the Japanese and the Burmese as well as the climate and topography of Burma and for every available report on the engagements fought against the Japanese as well as details of the enemy their methods of working and culture. He reviewed the risks of living and surviving in deep jungle and the need for adequate re-supply. He anticipated the opposition of three divisions, numbering some 30,000 men.

Modern management

10.3   This could be described as know your business so that you are able
to make effective judgements and decisions based upon best knowledge.
From many of the recent disasters it is evident that most senior
management did not know or understand the hazards that were prevalent
within their undertaking. If they had studied the master plan then they
failed to act upon it. In the case of Wingate, the success or failure of his
operations in terms of human loss were critical however, with modern
business activities, the element of identifying hazards has to some extent
been lost to accountants and risk management is primarily based on
finance.

Risk assessment

Wingate leadership

10.4   From the information Wingate requested he identified the hazards
the project would face and determined the risks. He evaluated the medical
problems his troops would encounter so that he could plan to reduce the
risks to an acceptable level. Once he had all the available information on
the hazards he assessed the risks. His people would be killed, injured and
become ill. He balanced the risks against the outcomes from success and
placed a value on it. He consulted with his senior officers but took
ownership of decisions.

Modern management

10.5   There are hazards that are highly visible to an undertaking's
activities and it is critical that an effective leader has that knowledge and
that it is not a delegated matter that the board is unaware of. Again, we
have seen that when senior management have been equipped with safety
critical information they have failed to act upon it. In war, enormous risks
are undertaken, but in peace we have seen the assessment of risk often fall
far short of public expectations.

Risk reduction

Wingate leadership

10.6   He did not have a dedicated safety advisor to proffer advice and
technical information so, what he did not know, he learnt from other
informed sources. If men unfamiliar with the jungle and all of its associated
risks were to succeed, then they needed to be prepared. Equipped with the

outcomes of the risk assessments he explored the options for reducing, or if possible, eliminating the risks. His personal leadership skills found answers to difficult questions and again he took ownership of high-level decisions. He did not hide behind regulations or 'how it has always been done before' options. His people mattered and he considered that they were the 'operation' because without them there would be no operation.

Modern management

10.7   We have witnessed that even when equipped with knowledge that there are risks, often of severe consequential outcomes, such as the *Herald of Free Enterprise*, *Piper Alpha* and the rail disasters, when there is no leadership to make decisions. To many it appears that people do not matter and that even if there is a disaster, people will still travel or work in hostile environments. In reviewing the multitude of disasters that have cost lives over recent years, nobody took ownership. Senior management must gather vital health and safety information from informed sources either in-house or externally and make use of it. Where there are risks, the workforce must be trained and a leader will need to identify the best training to meet the specific needs.

Identify and manage change

Wingate leadership

10.8   The key to Wingate's operation was flexibility and by good communication he could command his troops effectively. As intelligence was gathered he could identify changes that would allow rapid troop deployment. His force was divided into eight columns, each independent and through his leadership skills he could divert resources to where they were required. An attack may have required two, three or four columns to work together, then having achieved the objective, disperse back into their smaller columns – to re-group and re-supply, all while being hunted by the enemy forces.

Modern management

10.9   It would appear that in modern undertakings change can be a financial issue. Communication is selective and the use of information obtained by board members is often used as a 'hide it' option rather than deal with issues in an open and transparent way. This may be of immediate benefit to the undertaking but has no long-term value. Being able to manage change, particularly with regard to matters of health and safety are vital for an undertaking with true leadership management. The evidence suggests that when faced with a safety critical situation, senior management cannot give effective direction but leave it to those lower down the chain of command. Those same senior managers are quick to 'pass the buck' when things go wrong and management failure appears to be rewarded by a 'financial reward' followed by a sideways or promotional move to another undertaking.

Personnel

Wingate leadership

10.10   Wingate knew that his greatest asset was the troops who would enter the jungle and operate in the hostile environment. They had to believe in him as a leader and in what they were being asked to do. They were soldiers and obeyed orders, but that was not the issue; he wanted troops who would adapt and think for themselves. There were many occasions when there was nobody of real authority to make decisions and give orders. Wingate's British troops consisted of a large draft from the King's Liverpool Regiment and odds and ends from a dozen other regiments. They were nearly all married men, aged 28 to 35, from the smoky industrial areas of Northern England. They were wartime soldiers taken from coastal defence units at home and sent out to India to do garrison work. Most of them had expected to remain in that type of soldiering for the duration of the war. None of them had ever before been under fire. In addition, he had a Battalion of Gurkha Rifles, a Battalion of Burma Rifles, a Commando group, an RAF section, a signals section and a mule transport company. For most commanders it would have been an impossible task but for Wingate, with true leadership qualities, it was a task that could be accomplished.

Wingate was not surprised when he was told that no first class regiments could be spared for the job and, befitting his character, he accepted what was available and made the best of it. He assembled his men in the jungle for six months of rigorous training; the first part of it in the sweltering heat and torrential rain of the monsoon season. Whilst the men involved were soldiers and would do as ordered, he had to motivate 3,000 individuals who were not volunteers to undergo severe training. This cannot be accredited to military discipline and the success of the training came through leadership.

Modern management

10.11   There is an expression, 'it's the staff, you just cannot get good staff' and in many cases it may be justified, but often workers are given the minimum of training before being set to work and when things go wrong, the individual is blamed as being incompetent. Clearly, there is a case for sound training and a good safety culture will encompass individuals into a 'this is how we do it' safety attitude. What this shows is that a motivated workforce are able to achieve a great deal, often beyond what would normally be expected. This requires the leadership to be in touch and communicate to develop those undertaking all jobs in the undertaking to ensure that everybody follows the health and safety systems. It could be said that the workforce is only as good as senior management and there is some belief that in the modern workplace, people do not matter. Generally, those employed do as they are told or look for other employment. That cannot be a broad brush statement because there are many companies who value their workforce and have effective health and safety systems and procedures in place. Perhaps the concern is that there may be evidence that the poor performers outweigh the good performers and there is also a tendency to focus on bad practice and not to highlight good performance.

Training

Wingate leadership

10.12   The area in which the Chindits were to be trained was 35 miles from the nearest small town. It was the suffocating period just before the monsoon season when the temperature sometimes reaches 120 degrees in the shade. The conventional way of carrying out tactical training is on a table covered with sand modelled into miniature contours. Wingate derided this concept and ordered sandpits to be dug, 400 square yards in size. Men were represented by the tip of a match sticking out of the ground, forests by tiny pieces of bamboo. The Brigadier insisted that every hill, tree, river and gun emplacement should be built in exactly to scale of a 100 yards to 12 inches, and that every movement be timed with stop-watch precision so that an officer lying down in the sand-pit could clearly visualise the operation as a whole. In one of his training lectures, Wingate explained why he gave this painstaking attention to detail:

> 'Before a leader can discharge a task successfully he must picture that task being discharged. Every operation must be seen as a whole. By that I mean it must be seen pictorially as a problem in time and space. The chief difference between a good and a bad leader is that a good leader has an accurate imagination. Most commanders are unable to foresee accurately. Their minds present them with a series of pictures showing their commands moving victoriously from point to point. These pictures are completely bogus. The good commander requires an anxious, meticulously accurate and ever active imagination. By constantly insisting on scrupulous realism in the detail of his images, he will learn to picture only what he can perform and to reject all fancy.'

He knew that training was vital and personally took charge of every aspect of their training. He took second line troops and turned them into world-class jungle fighters – and that comes about not by giving orders but by leadership.

Modern management

10.13   Training for modern business can be expensive and, if not targeted, prove to be of little or no value. Training costs money and takes time which is lost to core business. Good sound training will ensure that the workforce is competent and onboard with the corporate philosophy for production targets within the confines of safe working practices. The leader needs to identify the 'right' training and ensure attendance because good training is excellent but poor training is, in fact, worse than no training at all.

Communication

Wingate leadership

10.14   Communications were the key to success or failure of the entire project. Not only did Wingate require effective links with the outside world, but he could communicate to even the most dispirited soldiers and lift them to new heights. The Brigadier held his early training lectures at dusk and the night would close in as he began speaking. He would group his officers and NCOs on the tiers of steps round the well and held forth to them under the stars with the old Hindu architecture of the Maharajah's hunting-lodge as a backcloth. Wingate knew that it was a stirring setting. After the first talk, in which Wingate explained how he wanted the men to be trained when they arrived, his officers went back to their tents with the exhilarating feeling of being on a great adventure.

At one point in the training period, Wingate received a report that morale was low in one of the companies. This group was made up of the oldest men, whose closest contact with outdoors had been a gentle game of cricket on the common on Saturday afternoons. Their sergeant major suggested to one of the officers that a brief pep talk by the Brigadier would accomplish wonders. It was a Saturday night when Wingate decided that he would address the men after the church service on Sunday morning. Next day, speaking without notes, he delivered an address that inspired every man in the force.

Modern management

10.15   Wingate had the advantage of military rank and could call on this attribute, however, in modern business the message has to come from a leader who can lead and to do so through communication. A modern example, whilst not health and safety related, was when there was a problem with one of the Virgin group of companies and Richard Branson was to be found in the midst of the trouble helping staff, answering questions and being visibly seen. Many would say that it was just a publicity exercise, which may well be the case, but the point is he was there and was seen to be participating. He was exposed to questions and confrontation.

Sending a message is not sufficient, the leader will want to know and ensure that the deliverable can be achieved. A vital link in any business is effective communication and when an effective leader communicates, people listen. It is then not just the boss giving orders but a leader giving direction. There is a great deal of difference.

Crucial co-operation

Wingate leadership

10.16 Wingate had insisted on having RAF flying officers attached to his force and on the ground so as to ensure the maximum chance of success for his daring scheme of co-operation between ground and air forces. The dropping of supplies was not new, but it was critical to the very survival of his troops. If supplies failed, the operation failed and men died. Never before had a force of several thousand men been tasked with the long range penetration of enemy territory relying solely on airborne supplies. Wingate also expected that, operating in the thick of Japanese troop concentrations, he would be able to relay to the RAF precise information as to what targets in Burma to bomb and when.

Modern management

10.17 A critical element of every undertaking is co-operation – whether it is internal or external. Delivering the health and safety message requires the co-operation of everybody in the undertaking. It involves not only senior management and employees but contractors who may be engaged to undertake work and a company that relies on others to provide services or goods will only be as good as its weakest link.

Leadership selection

Wingate leadership

10.18   Before any exercise was started, Wingate 'briefed' his officers as he would before a real engagement and was one of the very few Brigadiers who personally briefed his NCOs. After each exercise he received full reports from umpires and platoon commanders. Then he lectured the cadre on the mistakes made and the lessons learned. The phenomenal thoroughness of this training, whilst tough at the time, paid high dividends in confidence and morale and was largely responsible for the success of the operation. He had provided for the troops a sense of ownership of the operation, a belief in their abilities and trust that he could lead them not only into the operation but he could lead them back out. These were the elements of good leadership.

Wingate set an exacting standard for his officers and NCOs and was a hard commander to satisfy. During the training period he weeded out several officers on the ground that were good, but not good enough, and the only test of an officer was in the field of battle. His standpoint was that no officer should be allowed to hold a rank that he cannot carry in battle.

Modern management

10.19   This same philosophy should apply to management today because many managers can hold their position because of who they know, rather than their ability to lead by example and do the job.

Ownership and trust

Wingate leadership

10.20   Only a few troops were volunteers, the remainder were sent to do a job of soldiering. To achieve even the training element there was a need for ownership of the project and trust in Wingate, who would lead and direct them in some of the most hostile conditions known to man. Without this there would have been no operation.

Modern management

10.21   When the workforce has some form of ownership they develop a pride in what they do and that in turn reduces incidents. Linked to ownership is trust in senior management. Trust has to be worked at and distrust is easy to obtain. People would far prefer to be told the truth and cope with the outcome than fed information that has no foundation. Once trust is lost, loyalty follows and so do incidents as people become disinterested in what they do.

Lessons learned

Wingate leadership

10.22 Wingate was not content to have completed the operation. He wanted to know what lessons could be learned. He did this with as much consideration and care as he did when preparing for the operation. This is a critical aspect of good leadership; to identify failings and learn for the future. 3,000 men went into the jungle, 2,180 returned. They were all shattered and emaciated. On future operations he would ensure that there was a system for casualty evacuation which was the major cause of loss.

Modern management

10.23 An effective leader will not bury bad news but learn from it. Some think that to address an incident is admitting to failure, but it is better to put right a wrong than have two incidents to bury. As with Wingate, good leadership will identify failings so as to learn for the future.

Leadership Success

10.24 Every officer and man who served under Wingate worshipped him, yet he was a stern and exacting leader and never played for popularity. He won respect and admiration by example and achievement. In Burma, Wingate's officers, often operating individually and at great distances from Brigade Headquarters, found that every situation they ran into had been rehearsed in the Brigadier's sandpit exercises. After the first Chindit operation, Wingate spent time evaluating the successes and failures and learning from it, so that on the second operation the lessons learned were adopted and the successes were even greater. In conclusion, effective leadership is critical not only in war but in everyday modern business operations.

Safety leaders

10.25 It was identified in the Preface that there is a difference between leadership and management and the philosophy adopted by John Adair, whilst already quoted, is used again to establish the message as it is a most important point.

'You can be appointed a manager but you are not a leader until your personality and character, your knowledge and your skill in doing the functions of leadership are recognized by the others involved. This is the fundamental difference.'

It is the key elements of personality, character and knowledge that will form the basis of examination within the corporate health and safety concept. Personality is obviously an individual trait and everybody is different even though types of personalities can be placed in separate boxes. A good leader will have a personality that will be capable of delivering the message to every level of the workforce. It should, therefore, be the personality that achieves the objective and not his or her position of authority within the undertaking. An equally important element is an individual's character which often needs to be robust when dealing with health and safety. The word 'robust' is used and must not be compared with an individual who achieves through domination or bullying. It is the strength of character often combined with personality that will target and reach the objective. The final element is that of knowledge and nothing can be achieved if the leader does not know what is happening or how to target an objective. This can only be achieved through the knowledge of the undertaking's objectives in the wider sense, eg manufacturing output, sales targets and profit and loss boundaries. With the knowledge of the corporate function, the health and safety aspect can be contained within the day-to-day business.

It is often stated that senior management are responsible for health and safety and, therefore, must have detailed knowledge to adopt and manage it. That is not the case. A good leader will identify the status of health and safety within the undertaking and deploy the specialist knowledge of a health and safety advisor. The health and safety advisor can be an in-house employee or an external consultant. In either case, the role of the advisor is to provide senior management with information for them to implement. A good leader will provide skilled competent staff to perform the work of the undertaking. This extends to the health and safety advisor, whether an employee or a consultant, who must be recognised as being competent.

Personality of a leader

10.26 The leader can now be identified as having the personality to deliver the health and safety message to every level of staff and have the character that will be firm but fair in adopting. This will be supported through sound knowledge of what needs to be done, how to achieve it and how to ensure it remains active. This fundamental package of attributes is important and is all part of the key to success in leadership.

An effective leader will be able to adapt his or her style to suit a given situation, which can include such events as major changes in health and safety to the investigation of serious incidents. A manager can direct and give orders to subordinates, but it is leadership that will achieve a successful outcome. Those that are in the leadership model will hold the workforce together, particularly in difficult and stressful times. It is effective leadership that will respond to individual needs, identifying vulnerability, weaknesses and strengths. This leadership quality will enable the understanding of how people motivate themselves. While the emphasis is on health and safety, the qualities discussed above extend to all aspects of management and good leadership functions will include the following:

- the objectives with regard to health and safety can be effectively established through the health and safety policy;

- the policy should be considered as a contract between the senior manager and his employees and must be reviewed at regular intervals;

- as a minimum the policy must state his/her attention to provide adequate control of the health and safety risks arising from his/her company's work activities;

- to consult with his/her employees on matters affecting their health and safety;

- to provide and maintain safe plant equipment;

- to ensure the safe handling of substances;

- to provide information, instruction and supervision for employees;

- to ensure all employees are competent to undertake their tasks and to give them adequate training;

- to prevent accidents and cases of work-related ill health;

- to maintain safe and healthy working conditions;

- to review and revise the safety policy at regular intervals.

A series of detailed safety processes will need to be developed to support all of the high level policy statements and fundamental to the protection of employees is the identification of hazards in a work task, the assessment of the risk and the procedures to mitigate the risk and the system of working developed to ensure a safe operation. It must be recognised that these measures are being put in place to protect the employee and his input and involvement in the process is essential.

A leader needs to ensure effective communication with all members of staff. For example, he will talk to the workforce and understand their concerns and confirm controls in place are working, he will confirm equipment provided is fit for purpose, he will understand the substances used in the work processes, he will review on a regular basis the training requirements of his employees and continually strive to improve his safety processes.

A true safety leader will always be visible to his work force and he will ensure through first hand communication with his line management and workforce that the company safety system and processes achieve the objectives in his safety policy. Occasional involvement in the process of preparing of risk assessments will be noticed by the workforce and he can determine the effectiveness of the system first hand.

An organisation requires the leadership to establish the base-line foundations upon which the undertaking can function and they will be identified in the company's health and safety policy which should be written by the most senior person in the company because that person will have the authority to direct and lead the safety processes.

The safety policy must state how the company will protect its employees from harm in the course of their work and establish the basis for a positive safety culture if the effectiveness of the statements in the policy are measured. The senior manager who writes a policy to comply with the law is not a leader; a true leader will take the time to visit his work sites and understand first hand the risks to his employees and the controls that are in place. The uncommitted manager will write a policy to comply with the law; a safety leader will issue a policy with the intention of protecting his employees from harm.

Part of effective leadership is to ensure that the systems and procedures are adopted and meet the requirements of the undertaking and this is achieved through monitoring and evaluating. The safety leader will require his or her safety system and processes to be audited internally to confirm compliance and effectiveness and he or she should actively seek involvement in external safety audits.

Leadership elements

10.27 Health and safety leadership can be formed into elements that encompass the health and safety of the team and the safety and health of individuals. The principal element is the objective which is adopted by the staff as a group, which is in turn adopted by the individuals. The development of leadership also focuses on three elements:

- awareness;

- understanding; and

- skill.

The individual will have an awareness of the health and safety culture within the corporate entity. In fact, that awareness will encompass the broad spectrum of health and safety and the management factors including the implementation and monitoring process. Linked to being aware is that of understanding the health and safety issues. It extends to knowing the culture, its strengths and weaknesses. The evolution of health and safety culture is determined by the third element – the skill. The skill is key to effective leadership because it involves interpersonal skills and positive two-way communication and the ability to be direct, firm, calm and sensitive.

Leadership management identifies the functions that can be delegated to members of staff as opposed to junior management or supervisors. The delegation process allows employees to be accountable, democratic and develop self-management. It enables individuals to evolve their own form of leadership. This means that the more freedom the individual has in the decision process the less direct control the leader will need to exert. It follows that the more involvement in the decision process the greater their motivation to sign up to the process.

Leadership profile

10.28   The profile of the effective leader means that there is no place for the authoritative type of personality whose motivation is to use power and authority to achieve the objectives. It is the more democratic style of leadership that will achieve the objectives and positive outcomes.

A positive aspect is that a leader can use the model to monitor changes or developments. Everybody in the undertaking should have a sense of responsibility for the elements of the circles, but they are not accountable – the leader is. That does not detract from the decision-making process, which should be shared and which indicates that participation produces commitment.

Conclusion

10.29   No amount of words can make an individual encompass health and safety in their undertaking because it has to be cultural in nature and be an integral part of the overall activities. Those undertakings that bolt health and safety onto their business have singled out a specific issue. They think that they can determine the cost of implementation in order that they can balance the books for value. Such separation may identify a financial output, but it is not a true reflection of the wider picture.

If after reading this book, a manager, no matter his seniority, is still of the opinion that health and safety is a business add-on then the point is lost. In that situation you remain at the boss level and will have to suffer the consequences of when it goes wrong. Of course, the argument is 'well we have done it this way for 30 years and nothing has ever gone wrong', then statistically an accident is due. Further, it will cost and that may be a heavy fine, legal costs, higher insurance premiums and possibly no insurance and perhaps damage to equipment. If having read the book you are still at the 'boss' status then you need to go back to page one, start again and see where you failed to see the value of good health and safety in the workplace.

Those who decide that they are already leaders need to be careful and review the health and safety management systems to ensure that they are up to date and effective. The 'bosses' who aspire to become leaders will have their own thoughts of how they can progress change in their undertaking. It may be an uphill struggle, but the cultural difference within a positive undertaking has to be experienced and then leadership is attained.

Appendix A

Outline Training Programme

1. The benefits of a safe company to the employee.

2. Legislation.

3   How accidents occur.

4. Management of safety.

5. Risk management.

6. Change management.

7. Inspections, observations, audits and reviews.

8. Occupational health and hygiene

9. Incident/accident reporting notification and investigation.

10. Legislation specific to the employees' industry.

11. Human factors.

The above agenda will provide an overall basic training and the topics have been expanded to cover the content in the sections below.

1. The benefits of a safe company to employees

Few people appreciate the damage, both short and long-term, to their ability to make money if they are involved in an accident. This module should therefore cover the benefits of a positive safety culture to both the employee and the company and the downside of failure.

2. Legislation

Employees will benefit from an understanding of the legal framework in which they operate and the obligations of both the employer and employee.

2.1 Civil (common) law

The rule of common law is that 'everyone owes a duty to everyone else to take reasonable care so as not to cause them foreseeable injury'. Employers have duties at common law and all employers must provide a safe place of work including safe access and egress. This can be achieved through a safe system of work, safe plant and appliances and safe and competent fellow workers. Employees also have duties at common law in that they have to perform their work with reasonable care and skill.

These are implied terms of the contract of employment but, to a large extent, have been superseded by provisions laid down in criminal law (Employment Act 1978).

2.2 *Statutory (criminal) law*

The Health and Safety at Work etc Act 1974 (HSWA 1974) includes nearly everyone involved with work or affected by it. The requirements are built on general duties which are designed to encourage employers to improve organisation and systems. It seeks to involve employees through unions and better information and provide stronger powers for inspectors whilst creating a framework for developing and updating detailed safety law.

The training module should cover specific obligations including safety systems, safety policy, safety representatives and safety committees.

It should outline duties to those other than employees, duties to suppliers and, of course, duties of employees.

It will explain about the roles and responsibilities of the Health and Safety Commission (HSC) and the Health and Safety Executive (HSE) and the tools that they create and use to guide and regulate, such as Regulations (Statutory Instruments) and Codes of Practice. It will provide information about the powers such as enforcement, improvement and prohibition notices and prosecutions including aspects of personal liability.

2.3 *EC Legislation*

Although the UK has in place a comprehensive safety legislative regime based on the HSWA 1974, this is not necessarily the case in Europe .The EC has developed such a regime through the Framework Directive 89/39/EEC resulting in the Management of Health and Safety at Work Regulations 1992 (now superseded by the 1999 Regulations (SI 1999/3242)). In effect, both regimes now apply in the UK.

2.4 *The '6-pack'*

- Management of Health and Safety at Work Regulations 1999 (SI 1999/3242)

- Provision and Use of Equipment Regulations (PUWER) 1998 (SI 1998/2306)

- Personal Protective Equipment at Work Regulations (PPE) 1992 (SI 1992/2966)

- Manual Handling Operations Regulations 1992 (SI 1992/2793)

- Health and Safety (Display Screen Equipment) Regulations (DSE) 1992 (SI 1992/2792)

- Workplace (Health, Safety and Welfare) Regulations 1992 (SI 1992/3004) (onshore only)

The 'Framework Directive' 89/391/EEC provides a framework for the five key elements:

1. principles;

2. prevention of occupational risk;

3. protection of safety and health;

4. elimination of risk and accident factors;

5. informing, consulting, participation of workers representatives.

The Management of Health and Safety at Work Regulations 1999 has a number of key points. The prime tool for management to control health and safety is through risk assessment. This requires management to implement planning, organisation, control, monitoring and review of protective measures.

There must be effective health surveillance particularly where there is a known potential risk to employees. Management must engage competent health and safety advisors and provide employees with safety training.

Consideration must also be given to emergency procedures, escape and evacuation. Employers have to provide information regarding health and safety to employees, contractors and temporary workers and employees have to co-operate with the employer. Risk management is core to the approach.

3. How accidents occur

3.1 Definitions

- Accident – includes any undesired circumstances which give rise to ill health or injury damage to property, plant, products or the environment, production losses or increased liabilities.

- Incident – includes all undesired circumstances and near misses which have the potential to cause damage.

3.2 Accidents

Accidents occur through human factors where people for whatever reason undertake unsafe acts. There are environmental factors where there are unsafe conditions. In all cases there are underlying causes which may be attributed to a lack training or maintenance or poor training or maintenance or a failure to carry out inspections.

3.3 Root causes

A failure by management to identify the need to have or adopt an effective safety management system or a culture of poor procedures and practices or a failure to follow systems and procedures.

4. Management of safety

Managements role is to be proactive and set the Health and Safety Policy, establish the organisation and arrangements, provide competent people, good plant and equipment. They must motivate all employees and influence behaviour. They need to monitor the outcomes and modify as required.

5. Risk management

Risk management is fundamental to the HSWA 1974 and is the process to protect company assets, both human and material. This can be achieved through risk assessment. Every activity has some risk associated with it, such as crossing the road, driving a vehicle, air travel or working at height. People undertake the activity because they believe either the possible effect of the hazard is slight or the risk is acceptable.

To determine the risk in an activity, we consider the hazard and attempt to determine what could go wrong and, if it does go wrong, how serious are the consequences? There is then the probability which is expressed as:

Risk = Consequences (hazard effect) x Probability

Having determined the risk we decide on precautions, assess the residual risk and make a final assessment to proceed or not.

6. Change management

Many incidents result from poor management of change including drawings, procedures, software or people. Where change occurs a process must be put in place to control the change and to fully document it.

7. Inspections, observations, audits and reviews

Inspections and observations are proactive management tools. They can focus on equipment and physical conditions. Observations can focus on behaviour whilst audits focus on compliance with systems procedures and practices.

It is essential that reviews are made to ensure recommended changes have been implemented and are effective. The outcome is that the actions companies decide to make are undertaken in a certain way to make them safe and they must be conducted in this manner every time. Audits are the means for ensuring that this is the case.

Appendix B

Change Control Process

An example of a change control process is shown in a flowchart at Figure 2 below. The flowchart is the work of Phil Bradbury of Integrated Subsea Services and forms part of their safety management system. The flowchart describes the processes which are required to be adopted in Safety Management Systems. Such systems are invaluable in providing safe systems of work on a step-by-step basis for any project. In this case it is based on an offshore diving operation

1. The first step in providing good safety is to ensure that your services can support what a customer requires, therefore, during the contract review process you must confirm that you have the right people and equipment and their availability to complete the work. Any wrong step here may not only bring financial disaster, but also expose your workforce to unnecessary hazards and risks.

2. The second step is to ensure that a programme of work and specific work control processes are developed to ensure that the work can be completed safely. This is important as the information here forms the basis of instruction to operational personnel on the requirements for undertaking the work. It also helps to provide the safety performance requirements that are desired by the company and customer. It is at this stage that an element of guidance is also built into the work to help the operational team carry out work to your own and your customer's standards. This is usually done through the provision of Safety Plans and Bridging Documents which tie project activities and processes back into your company standards and those of the customer, therefore providing continuity of work practices and familiarity with safe working processes.

3. Before progressing the work, a hazard and risk analysis must be undertaken to ensure that the working environment within which project operations are taking place do not still contain potential hazards and risks after the specific work controls have been developed. At this stage it is advisable to look at the project on a broad basis and take each operation in chronological order. To ensure that safety of the worksite is maintained, the personnel taking

part in this Hazard/Risk Assessment should be those with familiarity of work operations, both at management and operational level. Any actions/changes arising out of a review will require recording and tracking to close out before operations start on that particular activity. This may require re-visiting and changing the specific work control processes described in item 2 above. However, once this is complete and changes have been confirmed and authorised, then progression to operations can take place.

4. It is at the boundary of the line from office engineering and Onshore Project Management to actual work operations where the most safety risks to an operation are present. This transition provides the site management team, supervisory staff and workforce with multiple exposures to potential hazards and risk if it is not managed correctly (eg new processes, familiarisation issues, new personnel, multiple simultaneous operations, new worksite, new equipment, schedule implications). Communication is a key element at this time and processes have to be in place which provide for the ease of transmitting information amongst the work team and to and from the office. As well as specific familiarisation activities, all the key processes as described in items 5 and 6 below help to manage and ensure safe working operations.

5. Once work activities are underway, information management is a key process that enables work to progress safely and efficiently. Providing the site management, supervisory staff and workforce with vehicles to enable this is paramount to providing good safety at the worksite. Daily operational planning should be discussed between all parties to ensure that in the next shift no surprise work operations are carried out between work groups. It is here that Permit to Work requirements should also be discussed and any changes to the operational programme are recorded and, if required, new risk and hazard analysis identified to be carried out to cater for the changes prior to work proceeding. Output from this avenue will be used to feed information back to office staff who can review work operations and identify any broader impact/change implications. In such cases work may have to be stopped whilst these impacts and changes are assessed. Instructions and guidance can also be transferred to the workforce from this meeting which co-ordinates the work activities of each site work team for the next period.

6. At the worksite, the management of safety is still a key requirement and supervisory staff must ensure that sufficient time is allotted to each work team to enable familiarisation with work processes.

Figure 3: Project Safety Process

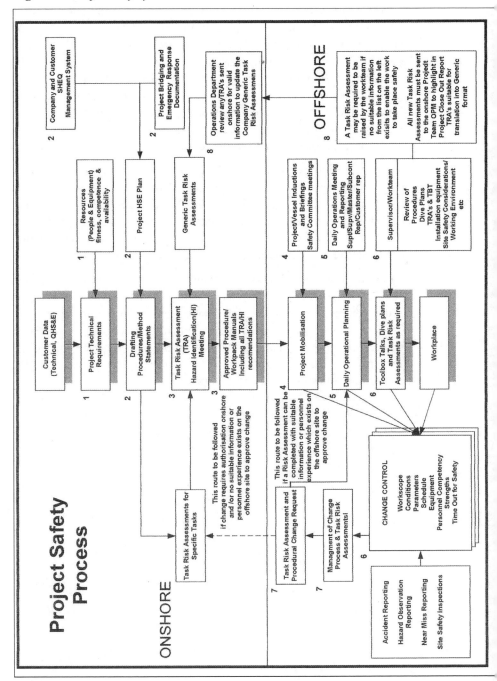

7.   Toolbox Talks provide a good venue where the team can get together and discuss the up and coming work programme. Again, at this time, any doubt about the work programme should be explored by the team, and where new or perceived hazards still remain then a site Risk Assessment should be undertaken. Changes may also need to be managed by the work team on a more local basis because of inputs from other areas, such as improvement information from Accident Reports and industry guidance etc. Changes may also be effected because of determination in the working environment, for example, conditions, time, individual competency, etc.

8.   If the activities in item 6 above results in a change to the work programme then this must be authorised by site management. This step is important as some element of the change may have broader implications on the safe operations of the worksite which the site team are not aware of and, therefore, any such change will require authorisation from the Onshore Project Management Team.

9. All the information which is generated by the site team should be fed back to the Onshore Project Management Team during or on completion of the job as the data contained in it can be used to refresh and improve on existing standards. Without this feedback loop, the Safety Management System will not operate efficiently and provide the level of safety at the worksite that can cater for the protection of employees and others.

Appendix C

Example Audit Interview Questions

Listed below are examples of possible audit interview questions for the President/MD of an offshore contractor. These questions are equally applicable in context to any undertaking.

- What are you personally doing to communicate to the work team that working safely and preventing pollution is a job priority?

- How are your employees informed of your company's HSE policy?

- What is your strategy to improve your company's safety performance?

- How do you ensure that subcontractors utilised by your organisation have HSE policies and HSE management systems that are in alignment with yours and ultimately the client?

- What have you done personally to ensure safety critical equipment supplied for your personnel is fit for the purpose?

- How are individuals and groups at worksite level encouraged to participate in solving HSE issues?

- How was your company informed of clients' HSE requirements?

- What HSE improvement targets do you have? How is achievement of these targets monitored and reported?

- What is the process for assessing subcontractors' HSE management capabilities?

- How do you communicate to your subcontractors your company's commitment to protecting people?

- How do you monitor undesirable trends from near miss reporting and mitigate against them?

- From current trends, what do you consider to be the greatest risks to your offshore teams?

- Are job descriptions available for each position (company and contractors)? Are HSE responsibilities clearly defined? How often are these reviewed?

- Do you and your staff have written safety roles and responsibilities? What are yours? What actions do you personally take to demonstrate safety leadership?

- How do you personally confirm permit to work systems designed to protect your offshore teams are effective?

- Do you personally review safety committee meeting minutes to determine effective close out of action items?

- What process do you have to obtain employee commitment to your HSE improvement process?

- Have you requested a review to be conducted of your workforce's belief in management attitudes to safety?

- How in your company are people trained to fill a position? Who is responsible for training?

- Is there an effective induction process in your company?

- What occupational health issues do your employees face?

- If your employees are not satisfied with safety measures in place, are they entitled to stop work and take steps to improve safety?

- Have you a robust management of change process?

- Have you an effective emergency response process? When was this last practised? What improvements were planned from this practise and have they been implemented?

- What is the process your company uses for the identification and control of hazards?

- How do you involve the people you are trying to protect in this process?

- Do you have an effective system for producing and communicating dive plans to your offshore teams and individual divers?

- How do you ensure your standards and procedures are current and appropriate?

- What measures do you personally take to ensure you are adopting best safety leadership practise within the contracting community?

- Do you have an annual HSE plan? What topics are covered in this? How do you verify completion of the plan?

- Do you have a process to feedback performance measures to subcontractors?

- What process do you have to learn of incidents and high potential near misses from your industry? How does your workforce learn from these?

- What process do you have for the effective review and close out of action items from HSE audits reviews and incident investigations?

- Do you sit in risk assessment meetings to determine the effectiveness of your processes?

- How many visits to your worksites do you plan to make this year?

- What process do you use to learn of the HSE concerns of your workforce?

- Is there a corporate process to review your HSE management system at intervals? Are all the management team involved in this review? When was it last conducted?

- What specific safety training have you undertaken?

This audit profile is not conclusive and there will be other questions appropriate to a specific operation or undertaking. It provides a flavour of the types of questions a client needs to ask a contractor and, in turn, that a contractor needs to obtain from a subcontractor.

INDEX